W.L. Miller

Fort Wayne
May 1967

MATRIX THEORY

for Electrical Engineers

A. MARY TROPPER M.Sc. Ph.D.

Queen Mary College, University of London

GEORGE G. HARRAP & CO. LTD

London Toronto Wellington Sydney

ADDISON-WESLEY PUBLISHING COMPANY, INC.

Reading, Massachusetts · Palo Alto · London

ENGINEERING SCIENCE MONOGRAPHS

GENERAL EDITORS

Prof. M. W. Humphrey Davies, B.Sc., M.Sc., M.I.E.E.

H. Tropper, Dip.Ing., Ph.D., A.M.I.E.E.

both of Queen Mary College, University of London

No. 1

Matrix Theory for Electrical Engineers

First published in Great Britain 1962
by GEORGE G. HARRAP & CO. LTD.
182 High Holborn, London W.C.1

U.S.A. Edition distributed by
Addison-Wesley Publishing Company, Inc.,
Reading, Massachusetts, U.S.A.
Printed in the United States of America

Preface

THE purpose of this book is two-fold. In the first place it provides a concise but comprehensive treatment of the elementary aspects of matrix algebra. This covers the topics that are included in the second and third year mathematics syllabus of all engineering students. Secondly it shows how these mathematical ideas can be applied to a number of problems in electric circuit theory. This is intended for the electrical engineering student but may be useful also to practising engineers who may not be familiar with the methods.

The first three chapters are devoted to the purely mathematical part of the book, which follows conventional lines. Matrices and the operations of addition and multiplication of matrices are defined, and the existence of a unique reciprocal of a non-singular matrix is established. This leads to a discussion of the solution of systems of linear equations and the idea of linear dependence. The important concepts of eigenvalues and eigenvectors are introduced, and it is shown how a large class of matrices may be reduced to diagonal canonical form. Throughout the text worked examples are given to illustrate the various techniques. In addition, for further exercise, a number of examples with answers is included.

The second part of the book deals with some of the more important applications to problems of circuit theory. It is shown how matrix algebra can be used in four-terminal network and line theory. Next, after a brief discussion of the topological concept of the linear graph, the connection matrices are introduced and their use illustrated by a few examples. Lastly the use of matrices in the treatment of three-phase networks is considered. It is hoped that the discussion of the above applications will provide the student with an adequate working knowledge so that he should have no difficulty in applying the method to other problems he may meet.

A.M.T.

Contents

CHAPTER 1

Matrix Algebra

In recent years matrix theory has been used to solve a wide variety of engineering problems. The considerable simplification achieved makes it worthwhile for the engineer to acquire some familiarity with matrix methods, especially since the solution of many of the most common problems requires only a small amount of theory.

1·1 Definition and notation

A matrix may be regarded either as an operator or as a rectangular array of numbers. If we introduce suitable definitions of the operations of addition, multiplication etc. we shall find that matrices obey most of the laws that govern the algebra of numbers. There are, however, certain laws, such as the commutative law for a product, that are not satisfied by matrices. In applications in later chapters we shall usually regard a matrix as an operator transforming one set of numbers into another set.

Consider the set of three simultaneous linear equations in three unknowns x, y, z

$$\begin{aligned} ax+by+cz &= p,\\ dx+ey+fz &= q,\\ gx+hy+kz &= r. \end{aligned}$$

These equations are completely specified by the three arrays of numbers

$$\begin{bmatrix} a & b & c \\ d & e & f \\ g & h & k \end{bmatrix}, \quad \begin{bmatrix} x \\ y \\ z \end{bmatrix} \quad \text{and} \quad \begin{bmatrix} p \\ q \\ r \end{bmatrix}.$$

An obvious simplification would be achieved by replacing x, y, z by x_1, x_2, x_3 and rewriting the equations, using a subscript notation as follows:

$$\begin{aligned} a_{11}x_1+a_{12}x_2+a_{13}x_3 &= b_1,\\ a_{21}x_1+a_{22}x_2+a_{23}x_3 &= b_2,\\ a_{31}x_1+a_{32}x_2+a_{33}x_3 &= b_3. \end{aligned} \qquad (1)$$

The corresponding arrays of numbers then become

$$\begin{bmatrix} a_{11} & a_{12} & a_{13} \\ a_{21} & a_{22} & a_{23} \\ a_{31} & a_{32} & a_{33} \end{bmatrix}, \quad \begin{bmatrix} x_1 \\ x_2 \\ x_3 \end{bmatrix} \quad \text{and} \quad \begin{bmatrix} b_1 \\ b_2 \\ b_3 \end{bmatrix}.$$

This notation has the great advantage that the subscripts of an element indicate the position of the element in the array. For example, a_{23} occurs in the second row and third column. By convention the first suffix always refers to the row number and the second to the column number. When an array contains only one column, e.g. $\begin{bmatrix} x_1 \\ x_2 \\ x_3 \end{bmatrix}$, we use only one subscript which refers to the row number. Similarly, if there is only one row, e.g. $[y_1 \quad y_2 \quad y_3]$, the single subscript refers to the column number. We can now write the equations in the slightly shorter form

$$\begin{bmatrix} a_{11} & a_{12} & a_{13} \\ a_{21} & a_{22} & a_{23} \\ a_{31} & a_{32} & a_{33} \end{bmatrix} \begin{bmatrix} x_1 \\ x_2 \\ x_3 \end{bmatrix} = \begin{bmatrix} b_1 \\ b_2 \\ b_3 \end{bmatrix}. \tag{2}$$

This is understood to be equivalent to the three equations (1). Each of the three arrays of elements is called a *matrix*.

$$\begin{bmatrix} a_{11} & a_{12} & a_{13} \\ a_{21} & a_{22} & a_{23} \\ a_{31} & a_{32} & a_{33} \end{bmatrix}$$

has three rows and three columns and is known as a three by three matrix (written 3×3) or a square matrix of order 3. Unlike a determinant, a matrix need not be square. The rectangular matrix

$$\begin{bmatrix} a_{11} & a_{12} & a_{13} \\ a_{21} & a_{22} & a_{23} \end{bmatrix}$$

is of order 2×3. $\begin{bmatrix} x_1 \\ x_2 \\ x_3 \end{bmatrix}$ is of order 3×1, since it contains three rows and only one column. A matrix containing only one column is usually known as a *column vector*. Similarly a matrix containing only one row is known as a *row vector*. For example $[y_1 \quad y_2 \quad y_3]$ is a matrix of order 1×3 or a row vector of order 3.

The first of the three equations (1) can be written in the form

$$[a_{11} \quad a_{12} \quad a_{13}] \begin{bmatrix} x_1 \\ x_2 \\ x_3 \end{bmatrix} = b_1.$$

The left-hand side, which is $a_{11}x_1+a_{12}x_2+a_{13}x_3$, is known as the *inner product* of the row vector $[a_{11} \quad a_{12} \quad a_{13}]$ and the column vector $\begin{bmatrix} x_1 \\ x_2 \\ x_3 \end{bmatrix}$. More generally, the inner product of the row vector $[\alpha_1 \quad \alpha_2 \quad \ldots \quad \alpha_n]$ of order n and the column vector $\begin{bmatrix} \beta_1 \\ \beta_2 \\ \vdots \\ \beta_n \end{bmatrix}$, also of order n, is defined to be $\alpha_1\beta_1+\alpha_2\beta_2+\cdots+\alpha_n\beta_n$. This inner product can also be written $[\alpha_1 \quad \alpha_2 \quad \ldots \quad \alpha_n] \begin{bmatrix} \beta_1 \\ \beta_2 \\ \vdots \\ \beta_n \end{bmatrix}$, where the row vector always appears on the left, and it exists only if the two vectors contain the same number of elements.

Let us now examine the matrix equation (2). We see that if we form the inner product of the first row of the matrix $\begin{bmatrix} a_{11} & a_{12} & a_{13} \\ a_{21} & a_{22} & a_{23} \\ a_{31} & a_{32} & a_{33} \end{bmatrix}$ and the column vector on the left and equate this product to the first element of the column vector on the right, we obtain the first of the equations (1). If we repeat this, using in turn the second and third rows of the matrix $\begin{bmatrix} a_{11} & a_{12} & a_{13} \\ a_{21} & a_{22} & a_{23} \\ a_{31} & a_{32} & a_{33} \end{bmatrix}$ and of the vector $\begin{bmatrix} b_1 \\ b_2 \\ b_3 \end{bmatrix}$, we obtain the second and third of the equations (1).

We can now simplify our notation still further. We denote the matrix $\begin{bmatrix} a_{11} & a_{12} & a_{13} \\ a_{21} & a_{22} & a_{23} \\ a_{31} & a_{32} & a_{33} \end{bmatrix}$ by **A**, but we must now specify the order of the matrix. $\begin{bmatrix} x_1 \\ x_2 \\ x_3 \end{bmatrix}$ is denoted by **X** and $\begin{bmatrix} b_1 \\ b_2 \\ b_3 \end{bmatrix}$ by **B**. The equations (2) now become

$$\mathbf{AX} = \mathbf{B},$$

where **A** is of order 3×3. **A** may be regarded as an operator transforming the vector **X** into the vector **B**. We notice that if the order of **A** is given it is not necessary to specify the orders of the vectors **X** and **B.** Since **A** has three columns, **X** must have three rows, or the inner products on the left-hand side of the equation would not exist. Thus **X** is of order 3. Again, since **A** has three rows there are three possible inner products of rows of **A** with **X**, so that **B** must have three rows. In much of the literature in pure mathematics column vectors are denoted by small letters to distinguish them from matrices that are not vectors. The matrix equation would then be written $\mathbf{Ax} = \mathbf{b}$. This, however, would be inconvenient in electrical engineering, as the reader will see when we come to consider some examples. We shall therefore use capital letters for all matrices and state specifically when they denote vectors.

In general, if **A** is a matrix of order $m \times n$, and **X**, **B** are column vectors of orders n, m respectively, the single matrix equation

$$\mathbf{AX} = \mathbf{B}$$

is equivalent to m linear equations in the n unknowns $x_1, x_2, \ldots, x_n$. To obtain the ith of these equations we equate to b_i the inner product of the ith row of **A** and the column vector **X**. This equation is

$$a_{i1}x_1 + a_{i2}x_2 + \cdots + a_{in}x_n = b_i,$$

or more briefly

$$\sum_{k=1}^{n} a_{ik}x_k = b_i.$$

1·2 Addition

Let **Y**, **Z** be two column vectors, both of order n. The column vector **W**, also of order n, whose elements are given by

$$w_i = y_i + z_i \quad (i = 1, 2, \ldots, n)$$

is defined to be the sum of **Y** and **Z**, and we write

$$\mathbf{W} = \mathbf{Y} + \mathbf{Z}.$$

If **Y** and **Z** are not of the same order their sum does not exist. This definition is analagous with a well-known result in geometry. If

$\vec{OP}$, $\vec{OQ}$ are two vectors whose sum is the vector $\vec{OR}$, and if P, Q, R have rectangular cartesian coordinates (x_1, y_1, z_1), (x_2, y_2, z_2), (x_3, y_3, z_3) respectively, O being the origin, then

$$x_3 = x_1+x_2,$$
$$y_3 = y_1+y_2,$$
$$z_3 = z_1+z_2.$$

Now suppose that $\mathbf{Y}=\mathbf{AX}$, $\mathbf{Z}=\mathbf{BX}$, where $\mathbf{A}$, $\mathbf{B}$ are both $m\times n$ matrices and $\mathbf{X}$ is a column vector of order n. Then $\mathbf{Y}$ and $\mathbf{Z}$ are both column vectors of order m and, if $\mathbf{W}=\mathbf{Y}+\mathbf{Z}$,

$$\begin{aligned} w_i &= y_i+z_i \quad (i = 1, 2,\ldots, m) \\ &= (a_{i1}x_1+a_{i2}x_2+\cdots+a_{in}x_n)+(b_{i1}x_1+\cdots+b_{in}x_n) \\ &= (a_{i1}+b_{i1})x_1+(a_{i2}+b_{i2})x_2+\cdots+(a_{in}+b_{in})x_n \\ &= c_{i1}x_1+c_{i2}x_2+\cdots+c_{in}x_n, \quad \text{say.} \end{aligned}$$

Thus $$\mathbf{W} = \mathbf{CX} = \mathbf{AX}+\mathbf{BX},$$

and it is natural to call the matrix $\mathbf{C}$ the sum of the matrices $\mathbf{A}$ and $\mathbf{B}$. Clearly

$$c_{ik} = a_{ik}+b_{ik} \quad (i = 1, 2,\ldots, m;\ k = 1, 2,\ldots, n).$$

The (i, k)th element of a matrix $\mathbf{A}$ is sometimes written $[\mathbf{A}]_{ik}$ and the matrix $\mathbf{A}$ is sometimes denoted by $[a_{ik}]$. We are thus led to the following definition:

If $\mathbf{A}$ *and* $\mathbf{B}$ *are two matrices of order* $m\times n$ *their sum* $\mathbf{A}+\mathbf{B}$, *also of order* $m\times n$, *is given by*

$$\mathbf{A}+\mathbf{B} = [a_{ik}+b_{ik}].$$

Alternatively we may write

$$[\mathbf{A}+\mathbf{B}]_{ik} = a_{ik}+b_{ik}.$$

Thus every element of the sum of two matrices is the sum of their corresponding elements. If $\mathbf{A}$ and $\mathbf{B}$ are not of the same order their sum does not exist. The definition given earlier of the sum of two vectors is the special case of this result when $n=1$.

1·3 Scalar multiplication

Suppose that $z_1=ky_1$, $z_2=ky_2,\ldots, z_m=ky_m$, where k is a scalar, i.e. an ordinary number, real or complex. We regard the vector $\mathbf{Z}$ of order m as being equal to k times the vector $\mathbf{Y}$ of order m, and we write $\mathbf{Z}=k\mathbf{Y}$. The reader will easily verify that if $m=3$ and (z_1, z_2, z_3),

(y_1, y_2, y_3) are rectangular cartesian coordinates this definition agrees with the corresponding result in geometry concerning the multiplication of a vector by a scalar. Now suppose that

$$\mathbf{Y} = \mathbf{AX},$$

where $\mathbf{A}$ is a matrix of order $m \times n$, so that $\mathbf{X}$ is a column vector of order n. Then we write

$$\mathbf{Z} = k\mathbf{Y} = k(\mathbf{AX}) = (k\mathbf{A})\mathbf{X}.$$

But direct substitution gives

$$\begin{bmatrix} z_1 \\ z_2 \\ \cdot \\ z_m \end{bmatrix} = \begin{bmatrix} ka_{11} & ka_{12} & \dots & ka_{1n} \\ ka_{21} & ka_{22} & \dots & ka_{2n} \\ \cdot & \cdot & \cdot & \cdot \\ ka_{m1} & ka_{m2} & \dots & ka_{mn} \end{bmatrix} \begin{bmatrix} x_1 \\ x_2 \\ \cdot \\ x_n \end{bmatrix},$$

so that the elements of the matrix $k\mathbf{A}$ are obtained by multiplying the corresponding elements of the matrix $\mathbf{A}$ by the scalar k. This is known as *scalar multiplication*. This definition includes that of scalar multiplication of a vector as a special case. Since it is immaterial whether we calculate first $\mathbf{AX}$ and then $k(\mathbf{AX})$, or first $k\mathbf{A}$ and then $(k\mathbf{A})\mathbf{X}$, we write without ambiguity

$$\mathbf{Z} = k\mathbf{Y} = k\mathbf{AX}.$$

In the particular case $k = -1$, we have

$$-\mathbf{A} = \begin{bmatrix} -a_{11} & -a_{12} & \dots & -a_{1n} \\ -a_{21} & -a_{22} & \dots & -a_{2n} \\ \cdot & \cdot & \cdot & \cdot \\ -a_{m1} & -a_{m2} & \dots & -a_{mn} \end{bmatrix}.$$

Hence if $\mathbf{A}$ and $\mathbf{B}$ are of the same order we have

$$\mathbf{A} - \mathbf{B} = \mathbf{A} + (-\mathbf{B})$$

and $$[\mathbf{A} - \mathbf{B}]_{ik} = a_{ik} + (-b_{ik}) = a_{ik} - b_{ik}.$$

If $\mathbf{B} = \mathbf{A}$, we have

$$[\mathbf{A} - \mathbf{A}]_{ik} = a_{ik} - a_{ik} = 0 \quad \text{for every } i \text{ and } k.$$

It is natural to regard $\mathbf{A} - \mathbf{A}$ as the *zero* (or null) matrix and denote it by $\mathbf{0}$, so that every element of $\mathbf{0}$ is zero. There are null matrices of all orders. Two matrices are defined to be *equal* if, and only if, they are of the same order and their difference is the zero matrix of that order. Thus every element of one matrix is equal to the corresponding element of the other.

EXAMPLE 1. Consider a 3-mesh circuit in which the impressed e.m.f.'s and the currents in the meshes are E_1, E_2, E_3; I_1, I_2, I_3. Then if Z_{ii} $(i=1, 2, 3)$ is the sum of the impedances of the ith mesh and Z_{ik} $(i \neq k)$ is the impedance common to the ith and kth meshes, then the equations on the mesh basis have the well-known form

$$E_1 = Z_{11}I_1+Z_{12}I_2+Z_{13}I_3,$$
$$E_2 = Z_{21}I_1+Z_{22}I_2+Z_{23}I_3,$$
$$E_3 = Z_{31}I_1+Z_{32}I_2+Z_{33}I_3.$$

These may be written in matrix form

$$\mathbf{E} = \mathbf{ZI},$$

where the 3×3 impedance matrix $\mathbf{Z}$ is given by $[\mathbf{Z}]_{ik}=Z_{ik}$. It is also well-known that

$$Z_{ik} = R_{ik}+pL_{ik}+\frac{1}{p}S_{ik},$$

where R_{ik}, L_{ik}, S_{ik} represent resistance, inductance, elastance respectively and $p=j\omega$, with the usual notation. Thus

$$\mathbf{Z} = \mathbf{R}+p\mathbf{L}+\frac{1}{p}\mathbf{S},$$

where $[\mathbf{R}]_{ik}=R_{ik}$ and similarly for $\mathbf{L}$ and $\mathbf{S}$, and

$$\mathbf{E} = \mathbf{ZI} = \mathbf{RI}+p\mathbf{LI}+\frac{1}{p}\mathbf{SI}.$$

1·4 Multiplication

If $\mathbf{A}$ is a matrix of order $m \times n$ and $\mathbf{B}$ is a matrix of order $n \times p$ the *product* $\mathbf{AB}$ is defined to be a matrix $\mathbf{C}$ of order $m \times p$, where c_{ik} is the inner product of the ith row vector of $\mathbf{A}$ and the kth column vector of $\mathbf{B}$. Thus

$$[\mathbf{AB}]_{ik} = \sum_{t=1}^{n} a_{it}b_{tk}.$$

The product $\mathbf{AB}$ exists only if the number of columns in the left-hand factor $\mathbf{A}$ is equal to the number of rows in the right-hand factor $\mathbf{B}$. Thus $\mathbf{A}$ and $\mathbf{B}$ may be such that $\mathbf{AB}$ exists, whilst $\mathbf{BA}$ does not exist. If $\mathbf{A}$ is of order $m \times n$ and $\mathbf{B}$ is of order $n \times m$, then $\mathbf{AB}$ and $\mathbf{BA}$ both exist. $\mathbf{AB}$ is square of order $m \times m$ and $\mathbf{BA}$ is square of order $n \times n$. If $m \neq n$ $\mathbf{AB}$ and $\mathbf{BA}$ are of different orders and cannot therefore be equal. Even if $m=n$, so that $\mathbf{AB}$ and $\mathbf{BA}$ are of the same order, $\mathbf{AB} \neq \mathbf{BA}$ in general. The two products may be equal in special cases and we then say that the matrices commute.

A *diagonal* matrix is a square matrix in which all elements are zeros except those in the principal diagonal (i.e. the diagonal running from the top left-hand to the bottom right-hand corner). Thus **A** is diagonal if, and only if, $a_{ik}=0$ $(i \neq k)$. Clearly two diagonal matrices of the same order always commute. The product is a diagonal matrix whose diagonal elements are the products of the corresponding diagonal elements of the two factors.

EXAMPLE 2.

(i) $$\mathbf{A} = \begin{bmatrix} 1 & 2 \\ -1 & 3 \end{bmatrix}, \qquad \mathbf{B} = \begin{bmatrix} -2 & 0 & 4 \\ 1 & 3 & -6 \end{bmatrix}.$$

$$\mathbf{AB} = \begin{bmatrix} 1 & 2 \\ -1 & 3 \end{bmatrix} \begin{bmatrix} -2 & 0 & 4 \\ 1 & 3 & -6 \end{bmatrix}$$

$$= \begin{bmatrix} 1\times-2+2\times1 & 1\times0+2\times3 & 1\times4+2\times-6 \\ -1\times-2+3\times1 & -1\times0+3\times3 & -1\times4+3\times-6 \end{bmatrix}$$

$$= \begin{bmatrix} 0 & 6 & -8 \\ 5 & 9 & -22 \end{bmatrix}.$$

BA does not exist.

(ii) $$\mathbf{A} = \begin{bmatrix} 1 & 2 \\ -1 & 3 \\ 5 & -2 \end{bmatrix}, \qquad \mathbf{B} = \begin{bmatrix} -2 & 0 & 4 \\ 1 & 3 & -6 \end{bmatrix}.$$

$$\mathbf{AB} = \begin{bmatrix} 1 & 2 \\ -1 & 3 \\ 5 & -2 \end{bmatrix} \begin{bmatrix} -2 & 0 & 4 \\ 1 & 3 & -6 \end{bmatrix} = \begin{bmatrix} 0 & 6 & -8 \\ 5 & 9 & -22 \\ -12 & -6 & 32 \end{bmatrix}.$$

$$\mathbf{BA} = \begin{bmatrix} -2 & 0 & 4 \\ 1 & 3 & -6 \end{bmatrix} \begin{bmatrix} 1 & 2 \\ -1 & 3 \\ 5 & -2 \end{bmatrix} = \begin{bmatrix} 18 & -12 \\ -32 & 23 \end{bmatrix} \neq \mathbf{AB}.$$

(iii) $$\mathbf{A} = \begin{bmatrix} 1 & 2 \\ -1 & 3 \end{bmatrix}, \qquad \mathbf{B} = \begin{bmatrix} -2 & 0 \\ 1 & 3 \end{bmatrix}.$$

$$\mathbf{AB} = \begin{bmatrix} 0 & 6 \\ 5 & 9 \end{bmatrix}, \qquad \mathbf{BA} = \begin{bmatrix} -2 & -4 \\ -2 & 11 \end{bmatrix} \neq \mathbf{AB}.$$

AB $\begin{bmatrix} (-2+2), & (0+6) \\ (+2+3), & (0+9) \end{bmatrix}$

(iv) $$\mathbf{A} = \begin{bmatrix} 1 & -4 & 2 \\ -2 & 8 & -4 \end{bmatrix}, \quad \mathbf{B} = \begin{bmatrix} 6 & 2 \\ 3 & -1 \\ 3 & -3 \end{bmatrix}$$

$$\mathbf{AB} = \begin{bmatrix} 0 & 0 \\ 0 & 0 \end{bmatrix} = \mathbf{0}.$$

This example shows that if $\mathbf{AB} = \mathbf{0}$ it does not necessarily follow that either $\mathbf{A} = \mathbf{0}$ or $\mathbf{B} = \mathbf{0}$.

Suppose that **A**, **B** are of orders $m \times n$, $n \times p$ respectively and **X**, **Y**, **Z** are column vectors of orders p, n, m respectively. Let $\mathbf{Y} = \mathbf{BX}$, $\mathbf{Z} = \mathbf{AY}$. Then

$$\begin{aligned} z_i &= a_{i1}y_1 + a_{i2}y_2 + \cdots + a_{in}y_n \quad (i = 1, 2, \ldots, m) \\ &= a_{i1}(b_{11}x_1 + b_{12}x_2 + \cdots + b_{1p}x_p) + a_{i2}(b_{21}x_1 + \cdots + b_{2p}x_p) \\ &\qquad + \cdots + a_{in}(b_{n1}x_1 + \cdots + b_{np}x_p) \\ &= (a_{i1}b_{11} + a_{i2}b_{21} + \cdots + a_{in}b_{n1})x_1 \\ &\qquad + (a_{i1}b_{12} + a_{i2}b_{22} + \cdots + a_{in}b_{n2})x_2 \\ &\qquad + \cdots + (a_{i1}b_{1p} + a_{i2}b_{2p} + \cdots + a_{in}b_{np})x_p. \end{aligned}$$

We may therefore write

$$z_i = c_{i1}x_1 + c_{i2}x_2 + \cdots + c_{ip}x_p \quad (i = 1, 2, \ldots, m)$$

where $c_{i1} = [a_{i1} \quad a_{i2} \quad \ldots \quad a_{in}] \begin{bmatrix} b_{11} \\ b_{21} \\ \vdots \\ b_{n1} \end{bmatrix}$,

$$c_{i2} = [a_{i1} \quad a_{i2} \quad \ldots \quad a_{in}] \begin{bmatrix} b_{12} \\ b_{22} \\ \vdots \\ b_{n2} \end{bmatrix},$$

$$\cdots\cdots\cdots\cdots$$

$$c_{ip} = [a_{i1} \quad a_{i2} \quad \ldots \quad a_{in}] \begin{bmatrix} b_{1p} \\ b_{2p} \\ \vdots \\ b_{np} \end{bmatrix}.$$

Thus for $k = 1, 2, \ldots, p$ it follows that c_{ik} is the inner product of the ith row of **A** and the kth column of **B**, and hence

$$\mathbf{Z} = \mathbf{CX} \quad \text{where} \quad \mathbf{C} = \mathbf{AB};$$

i.e. $$\mathbf{Z} = \mathbf{AY} = \mathbf{A(BX)} = \mathbf{(AB)X}.$$

Let **A**, **B**, **C** be matrices of order $m \times n$, $n \times p$, $p \times q$ respectively. Then **AB**, **BC** both exist and are of orders $m \times p$, $n \times q$ respectively and (**AB**)**C**, **A**(**BC**) both exist and are both of order $m \times q$. The reader will easily verify that

$$(\mathbf{AB})\mathbf{C} = \mathbf{A}(\mathbf{BC})$$

and there is therefore no ambiguity in writing the product **ABC**. This result can be extended to the product of any number of matrices, provided that the product exists, but it is important to note that we must not alter the order in which the factors occur.

If **A** and **B** are both of order $m \times n$ and **C** is of order $n \times p$, then **AC**, **BC** are both of order $m \times p$ and we have

$$\begin{aligned} [(\mathbf{A}+\mathbf{B})\mathbf{C}]_{ik} &= \sum_{t=1}^{n} (a_{it}+b_{it})c_{tk} \\ &= \sum_{t=1}^{n} a_{it}c_{tk} + \sum_{t=1}^{n} b_{it}c_{tk} \\ &= [\mathbf{AC}]_{ik} + [\mathbf{BC}]_{ik}. \end{aligned}$$

Thus $$(\mathbf{A}+\mathbf{B})\mathbf{C} = \mathbf{AC}+\mathbf{BC}.$$

Similarly, if **D** is of order $q \times m$,

$$\mathbf{D}(\mathbf{A}+\mathbf{B}) = \mathbf{DA}+\mathbf{DB}.$$

1·5 The unit matrix — OR IDENTITY MATRIX

We already have a matrix which corresponds in matrix algebra to the number zero in the algebra of numbers. We now need a matrix **1** to take the place of the number unity. **1** must have the property that $\mathbf{1A}=\mathbf{A}$ for every **A**, whenever the product on the left exists. Consider the diagonal matrix $\mathbf{1}_m$ of order $m \times m$ whose diagonal elements are all equal to unity.

$$\mathbf{1}_m = \begin{bmatrix} 1 & 0 & 0 & \dots & 0 \\ 0 & 1 & 0 & \dots & 0 \\ 0 & 0 & 1 & \dots & 0 \\ \cdot & \cdot & \cdot & \cdot & \cdot \\ 0 & 0 & 0 & \dots & 1 \end{bmatrix}.$$

The elements of this matrix are usually denoted by the Kronecker delta δ_{ik}, which is such that

$$\delta_{ik} = 0 \quad (i \neq k), \qquad \delta_{ii} = 1.$$

Then

$$[\mathbf{1}_m\mathbf{A}]_{ik} = \sum_{t=1}^{m} \delta_{it}a_{tk} = \delta_{ii}a_{ik} = a_{ik},$$

so that $\mathbf{1}_m\mathbf{A}=\mathbf{A}$ for any matrix $\mathbf{A}$ of order $m \times n$. The matrix $\mathbf{1}_m$ is called the *unit matrix* of order m, and there are unit matrices of all (square) orders. We do not usually specify the order unless it is necessary to avoid ambiguity, but we simply write $\mathbf{1}$. The reader should verify that $\mathbf{A}\mathbf{1}_n=\mathbf{A}$, and that, for any particular $\mathbf{1}$, $\mathbf{1}^2=\mathbf{1}^3=\cdots=\mathbf{1}^p=\mathbf{1}$, where p is any positive integer. $\mathbf{1}^3$ denotes $\mathbf{1}.\mathbf{1}.\mathbf{1}$ etc.

1·6 Scalar matrices

A matrix of the form $\lambda\mathbf{1}$, where λ is a scalar, is called a *scalar matrix*. Thus

$$\lambda\mathbf{1}_3 = \begin{bmatrix} \lambda & 0 & 0 \\ 0 & \lambda & 0 \\ 0 & 0 & \lambda \end{bmatrix}$$

is a scalar matrix of order 3. If $\mathbf{A}$ is of order $m \times n$ then

$$\lambda\mathbf{1}_m.\mathbf{A} = \lambda\mathbf{A} = \mathbf{A}.\lambda\mathbf{1}_n,$$

so that multiplication by a scalar matrix is equivalent to multiplication by a scalar, as defined in §1·3.

1·7 Transposition

The matrix obtained from $\mathbf{A}$ by interchanging its rows and columns is called the *tranpose* of $\mathbf{A}$ and is denoted by $\mathbf{A}^t$. If $\mathbf{A}$ is of order $m \times n$, $\mathbf{A}^t$ is of order $n \times m$ and

$$a_{ik}^t = a_{ki}.$$

The transpose of a column vector

$$\mathbf{X} = \begin{bmatrix} x_1 \\ x_2 \\ \vdots \\ x_n \end{bmatrix} \quad \text{is a row vector} \quad \mathbf{X}^t = [x_1 \quad x_2 \quad \ldots \quad x_n].$$

For convenience in printing we write a column vector horizontally as follows:

$$\mathbf{X} = \{x_1 \quad x_2 \quad \ldots \quad x_n\}.$$

Henceforward row vectors will always be written in the form $\mathbf{X}^t$, $\mathbf{Y}^t$ etc., where $\mathbf{X}$, $\mathbf{Y}$ are column vectors. Thus when a symbol $\mathbf{X}$ represents a vector it will always be a column vector.

Let **A**, **B** be of orders $m \times n$, $n \times p$ respectively. Then $\mathbf{C}=\mathbf{AB}$ exists and is of order $m \times p$. Moreover

$$c^t_{ik} = c_{ki} = \sum_{h=1}^{n} a_{kh}b_{hi} = \sum_{h=1}^{n} b^t_{ih}a^t_{hk}.$$

i.e.

$$[\mathbf{C}^t]_{ik} = [\mathbf{B}^t\mathbf{A}^t]_{ik},$$

or

$$\mathbf{C}^t = \mathbf{B}^t\mathbf{A}^t = (\mathbf{AB})^t.$$

Thus *the transpose of the product of two matrices is equal to the product of their transposes in the reverse order.*

1·8 The determinant of a square matrix

The determinant whose rows (and hence also columns) are identical with those of a given square matrix **A** is called the *determinant* of **A** and denoted by $|\mathbf{A}|$ (or sometimes $\det \mathbf{A}$). If $|\mathbf{A}|=0$, **A** is said to be *singular*. If $|\mathbf{A}| \neq 0$ it is *non-singular*. The value of a determinant is well-known to be unaltered by the interchange of rows and columns, so that $|\mathbf{A}^t|=|\mathbf{A}|$. Now the rule (or one of the four possible rules) for multiplying two determinants of the same order is precisely the rule for multiplying two square matrices of the same order. Hence

$$|\mathbf{AB}| = |\mathbf{A}| \times |\mathbf{B}|$$

if **A** and **B** are both square and of the same order. Moreover $|\mathbf{AB}| = |\mathbf{BA}|$, even though $\mathbf{AB} \neq \mathbf{BA}$ in general.

1·9 Minors and cofactors

If in any determinant $|\mathbf{A}|$ of order n we delete the row and the column containing the element a_{ik} we obtain a new determinant of order $n-1$, called the *minor* of a_{ik} and denoted by $\mathfrak{a}_{ik}$. We define the *cofactor* of the element a_{ik} to be $(-1)^{i+k}\mathfrak{a}_{ik}$ and denote it by A_{ik}. The following results are well-known.

(i) If we take the elements in any row of a determinant, multiply each by its cofactor and add the products, the sum is equal to the value of the determinant. Thus

$$\sum_{k=1}^{n} a_{ik}A_{ik} = |\mathbf{A}|. \tag{3}$$

(ii) If we take the elements in any row of a determinant and the cofactors of another row, multiply each element by the corresponding cofactor and add the products, the sum is zero. Thus

$$\sum_{k=1}^{n} a_{ik}A_{hk} = 0 \quad (h \neq i). \tag{4}$$

Corresponding results hold for columns.

1·10 The adjoint matrix

Let us replace every element a_{ik} of a matrix **A** by its cofactor in $|\mathbf{A}|$, viz. by A_{ik}, and then transpose the resulting matrix. The matrix obtained in this way is called the *adjoint matrix* of **A** and is denoted by adj **A**. Thus

$$[\text{adj } \mathbf{A}]_{ik} = A_{ki}.$$

We now form the product of the $n \times n$ matrix **A** and its adjoint matrix.

$$[\mathbf{A}.\text{adj } \mathbf{A}]_{ih} = \sum_{k=1}^{n} a_{ik}[\text{adj } \mathbf{A}]_{kh} = \sum_{k=1}^{n} a_{ik}A_{hk}.$$

Thus, using equations (3) and (4) we have

$$[\mathbf{A}.\text{adj } \mathbf{A}]_{ih} = 0 \quad (i \neq h)$$

and

$$[\mathbf{A}.\text{adj } \mathbf{A}]_{ii} = \sum_{k=1}^{n} a_{ik}A_{ik} = |\mathbf{A}|.$$

We see, therefore, that **A**(adj **A**) is a scalar matrix, all of whose non-zero elements are equal to $|\mathbf{A}|$. In the same way, using the results for columns analogous to equations (3) and (4), we can show that (adj **A**)**A** is equal to the same scalar matrix. Hence

$$\mathbf{A}(\text{adj } \mathbf{A}) = (\text{adj } \mathbf{A})\mathbf{A} = |\mathbf{A}|\mathbf{1}, \tag{5}$$

where **1** is the unit matrix of order n.

1·11 The reciprocal of a matrix

We now seek a matrix that will play the part in matrix algebra of the *reciprocal* of a given matrix. We therefore seek a matrix $\mathbf{A}^{-1}$ such that

$$\mathbf{A}.\mathbf{A}^{-1} = \mathbf{A}^{-1}.\mathbf{A} = \mathbf{1},$$

1 being a unit matrix. In order that both products $\mathbf{A}.\mathbf{A}^{-1}$ and $\mathbf{A}^{-1}.\mathbf{A}$ shall exist, **A**, $\mathbf{A}^{-1}$ must be of orders $m \times n$, $n \times m$ respectively. The two products are then of orders $m \times m$, $n \times n$ respectively, so that they cannot both be equal to the same unit matrix unless $m = n$. It follows that **A** and $\mathbf{A}^{-1}$ must both be square, so that we cannot define the reciprocal of a matrix unless it is square. It is clear that if **A** is singular, $\mathbf{A}^{-1}$ cannot exist. For if it does

$$|\mathbf{A}.\mathbf{A}^{-1}| = |\mathbf{A}|.|\mathbf{A}^{-1}| = 0.$$

On the other hand

$$|\mathbf{A}.\mathbf{A}^{-1}| = |\mathbf{1}| = 1,$$

giving a contradiction. If $\mathbf{A}$ is a non-singular $n \times n$ matrix, so that $|\mathbf{A}| \neq 0$, equation (5) shows that

$$\mathbf{A}\left(\frac{1}{|\mathbf{A}|}\text{ adj }\mathbf{A}\right) = \left(\frac{1}{|\mathbf{A}|}\text{ adj }\mathbf{A}\right)\mathbf{A} = \mathbf{1},$$

and hence we may take $\mathbf{A}^{-1} = (1/|\mathbf{A}|)$ adj $\mathbf{A}$. The question now arises whether this reciprocal is unique. Does there exist a matrix $\mathbf{B}$, different from $\mathbf{A}^{-1} = (1/|\mathbf{A}|)$ adj $\mathbf{A}$, such that $\mathbf{AB} = \mathbf{1}$? We can show that this is not the case. For, if $\mathbf{AB} = \mathbf{1}$,

$$\mathbf{A}(\mathbf{A}^{-1} - \mathbf{B}) = \mathbf{AA}^{-1} - \mathbf{AB} = \mathbf{1} - \mathbf{1} = \mathbf{0},$$

and
$$\mathbf{A}^{-1}\{\mathbf{A}(\mathbf{A}^{-1} - \mathbf{B})\} = \mathbf{A}^{-1}\mathbf{0} = \mathbf{0}.$$

But
$$\mathbf{A}^{-1}\{\mathbf{A}(\mathbf{A}^{-1} - \mathbf{B})\} = (\mathbf{A}^{-1}\mathbf{A})(\mathbf{A}^{-1} - \mathbf{B}) = \mathbf{1}(\mathbf{A}^{-1} - \mathbf{B}) = \mathbf{A}^{-1} - \mathbf{B}.$$

Hence
$$\mathbf{A}^{-1} - \mathbf{B} = \mathbf{0}, \quad \text{or} \quad \mathbf{B} = \mathbf{A}^{-1}.$$

We have used in the above a special case of a result that holds more generally. We have shown earlier that $\mathbf{AB} = \mathbf{0}$ does not necessarily imply $\mathbf{A} = \mathbf{0}$ or $\mathbf{B} = \mathbf{0}$. *If*, however, $\mathbf{AB} = \mathbf{0}$ *and* $\mathbf{A}$ *is square and non-singular, then* $\mathbf{B} = \mathbf{0}$. For $\mathbf{A}^{-1}$ exists, so that

$$\mathbf{A}^{-1}(\mathbf{AB}) = \mathbf{A}^{-1}\mathbf{0} = \mathbf{0}$$

and
$$\mathbf{A}^{-1}(\mathbf{AB}) = (\mathbf{A}^{-1}\mathbf{A})\mathbf{B} = \mathbf{1B} = \mathbf{B}.$$

Thus $\mathbf{B} = \mathbf{0}$. Similarly if $\mathbf{B}$ is square and non-singular and $\mathbf{AB} = \mathbf{0}$, then $\mathbf{A} = \mathbf{0}$.

We have now established that a square non-singular matrix $\mathbf{A}$ has a unique reciprocal $\mathbf{A}^{-1}$ of the same order given by

$$a_{ik}^{-1} = \frac{A_{ki}}{|\mathbf{A}|}.$$

When $\mathbf{A}$ is a 2×2 matrix the form of $\mathbf{A}^{-1}$ is very simple.

If $\mathbf{A} = \begin{bmatrix} a_{11} & a_{12} \\ a_{21} & a_{22} \end{bmatrix}$, $\quad A_{11} = a_{22}, \quad A_{22} = a_{11}, \quad A_{12} = -a_{21}, \quad A_{21} = -a_{12}.$

Thus adj $\mathbf{A} = \begin{bmatrix} A_{11} & A_{21} \\ A_{12} & A_{22} \end{bmatrix} = \begin{bmatrix} a_{22} & -a_{12} \\ -a_{21} & a_{11} \end{bmatrix}$

and
$$\mathbf{A}^{-1} = \frac{1}{|\mathbf{A}|}\text{ adj }\mathbf{A} = \frac{1}{a_{11}a_{22} - a_{12}a_{21}}\begin{bmatrix} a_{22} & -a_{12} \\ -a_{21} & a_{11} \end{bmatrix}.$$

EXAMPLE 3.

(i)
$$\mathbf{A} = \begin{bmatrix} 2 & -1 \\ 5 & 3 \end{bmatrix}, \qquad |\mathbf{A}| = 11.$$

$$\mathbf{A}^{-1} = \frac{1}{11}\begin{bmatrix} 3 & 1 \\ -5 & 2 \end{bmatrix} = \begin{bmatrix} 3/11 & 1/11 \\ -5/11 & 2/11 \end{bmatrix}.$$

(ii)
$$\mathbf{A} = \begin{bmatrix} 1 & 2 & 3 \\ 2 & -1 & 4 \\ 0 & -1 & 1 \end{bmatrix}, \qquad |\mathbf{A}| = \begin{vmatrix} 1 & 2 & 3 \\ 0 & -5 & -2 \\ 0 & -1 & 1 \end{vmatrix} = -7.$$

$$\mathbf{A}_{11} = (-1)^2\begin{vmatrix} -1 & 4 \\ -1 & 1 \end{vmatrix} = 3, \qquad A_{12} = (-1)^3\begin{vmatrix} 2 & 4 \\ 0 & 1 \end{vmatrix} = -2 \text{ etc.}$$

$$\mathbf{A}^{-1} = -\frac{1}{7}\,\text{adj}\,\mathbf{A} = -\frac{1}{7}\begin{bmatrix} 3 & -5 & 11 \\ -2 & 1 & 2 \\ -2 & 1 & -5 \end{bmatrix}.$$

The reader will easily verify that

$$\mathbf{A}^{-1}\mathbf{A} = -\frac{1}{7}\begin{bmatrix} 3 & -5 & 11 \\ -2 & 1 & 2 \\ -2 & 1 & -5 \end{bmatrix}\begin{bmatrix} 1 & 2 & 3 \\ 2 & -1 & 4 \\ 0 & -1 & 1 \end{bmatrix}$$

$$= -\frac{1}{7}\begin{bmatrix} -7 & 0 & 0 \\ 0 & -7 & 0 \\ 0 & 0 & -7 \end{bmatrix} = \begin{bmatrix} 1 & 0 & 0 \\ 0 & 1 & 0 \\ 0 & 0 & 1 \end{bmatrix} = \mathbf{1}.$$

1·12 Solution of linear equations

Consider a set of n simultaneous linear equations in the n unknowns $x_1, x_2, \ldots, x_n$. These may be written in matrix form

$$\mathbf{AX} = \mathbf{B}, \tag{6}$$

where $\mathbf{A}$ is an $n \times n$ matrix and $\mathbf{X}$, $\mathbf{B}$ are column vectors of order n. Suppose further that $\mathbf{A}$ is non-singular, so that $\mathbf{A}^{-1}$ exists. We may then pre-multiply both sides of equation (6) by $\mathbf{A}^{-1}$, giving

$$\mathbf{A}^{-1}(\mathbf{AX}) = \mathbf{A}^{-1}\mathbf{B}.$$

But
$$\mathbf{A}^{-1}(\mathbf{AX}) = (\mathbf{A}^{-1}\mathbf{A})\mathbf{X} = \mathbf{1X} = \mathbf{X},$$

and hence
$$\mathbf{X} = \mathbf{A}^{-1}\mathbf{B}.$$

We have now solved the equations (6).

EXAMPLE 4. Solve the equations

$$x_1+2x_2+3x_3 = 5,$$
$$2x_1- x_2+4x_3 = 11,$$
$$- x_2+ x_3 = 3.$$

These may be written $\mathbf{AX}=\mathbf{B}$, where

$$\mathbf{A} = \begin{bmatrix} 1 & 2 & 3 \\ 2 & -1 & 4 \\ 0 & -1 & 1 \end{bmatrix}, \qquad \mathbf{X} = \{x_1 \quad x_2 \quad x_3\}, \qquad \mathbf{B} = \{5 \quad 11 \quad 3\}.$$

In §1·11, Example 3 (ii), we found that

$$\mathbf{A}^{-1} = -\frac{1}{7}\begin{bmatrix} 3 & -5 & 11 \\ -2 & 1 & 2 \\ -2 & 1 & -5 \end{bmatrix}.$$

Hence

$$\mathbf{X} = \mathbf{A}^{-1}\mathbf{B} = -\frac{1}{7}\begin{bmatrix} 3 & -5 & 11 \\ -2 & 1 & 2 \\ -2 & 1 & -5 \end{bmatrix}\begin{bmatrix} 5 \\ 11 \\ 3 \end{bmatrix} = -\frac{1}{7}\begin{bmatrix} -7 \\ 7 \\ -14 \end{bmatrix} = \begin{bmatrix} 1 \\ -1 \\ 2 \end{bmatrix},$$

and $x_1=1$, $x_2=-1$, $x_3=2$.

1·13 The reciprocal of a transpose

Let $\mathbf{A}$ be square and non-singular, so that $\mathbf{A}^{-1}$ exists and $\mathbf{AA}^{-1}=\mathbf{1}$. Moreover $\mathbf{A}^t$ is also non-singular.

Now $(\mathbf{AA}^{-1})^t=\mathbf{1}^t=\mathbf{1}$.

But, by §1·7,

$$(\mathbf{AA}^{-1})^t = (\mathbf{A}^{-1})^t\mathbf{A}^t, \quad \text{and therefore} \quad (\mathbf{A}^{-1})^t\mathbf{A}^t = \mathbf{1}.$$

It follows that *the unique reciprocal of* $\mathbf{A}^t$ *is* $(\mathbf{A}^{-1})^t$ and we may write

$$(\mathbf{A}^t)^{-1} = (\mathbf{A}^{-1})^t.$$

Thus *the reciprocal of the transpose of a matrix is the transpose of its reciprocal.*

1·14 The reciprocal of a product

Let $\mathbf{A}$ and $\mathbf{B}$ be two non-singular square matrices of the same order. Then $\mathbf{A}^{-1}$ and $\mathbf{B}^{-1}$ exist, and

$$(\mathbf{AB})(\mathbf{B}^{-1}\mathbf{A}^{-1}) = \mathbf{A}(\mathbf{BB}^{-1})\mathbf{A}^{-1} = \mathbf{A1A}^{-1} = \mathbf{AA}^{-1} = \mathbf{1}.$$

It follows that the unique reciprocal of **AB** is $\mathbf{B}^{-1}\mathbf{A}^{-1}$. The method can obviously be extended to show that, if **C** is also of the same order and non-singular,

$$(\mathbf{ABC})^{-1} = \mathbf{C}^{-1}\mathbf{B}^{-1}\mathbf{A}^{-1}.$$

More generally, *the reciprocal of the product of any finite number of non-singular square matrices of the same order is the product of their reciprocals taken in the reverse order.*

This chapter will be concluded with some worked examples.

EXAMPLE 5. Find all the 2×2 matrices **X** satisfying the equation $\mathbf{X}^2=\mathbf{1}$.

The equation may be written

$$(\mathbf{X}-\mathbf{1})(\mathbf{X}+\mathbf{1}) = \mathbf{0}.$$

Clearly $\mathbf{X}=\mathbf{1}$ and $\mathbf{X}=-\mathbf{1}$ are solutions but, as we have seen in Example 2 (iv), there may be other solutions.

$$\text{Let}\quad \mathbf{X} = \begin{bmatrix} a & b \\ c & d \end{bmatrix}, \quad \text{so that}\quad \mathbf{X}^2 = \begin{bmatrix} a^2+bc & b(a+d) \\ c(a+d) & bc+d^2 \end{bmatrix}.$$

The equation $\mathbf{X}^2=\mathbf{1}$ is then equivalent to the four equations

$$a^2+bc-1 = 0,$$
$$b(a+d) = 0,$$
$$c(a+d) = 0,$$
$$bc+d^2-1 = 0.$$

If $b=0$ we must have $a^2=d^2=1$, $c(a+d)=0$. Thus $a=d=1$, $c=0$; $a=d=-1$, $c=0$; $a=1$, $d=-1$, c arbitrary; $a=-1$, $d=1$, c arbitrary. There are four similar possibilities if $c=0$. Hence the possible values for **X** are

$$\begin{bmatrix} 1 & 0 \\ 0 & 1 \end{bmatrix}, \quad \begin{bmatrix} -1 & 0 \\ 0 & -1 \end{bmatrix}, \quad \begin{bmatrix} 1 & 0 \\ c & -1 \end{bmatrix},$$

$$\begin{bmatrix} -1 & 0 \\ c & 1 \end{bmatrix}, \quad \begin{bmatrix} 1 & b \\ 0 & -1 \end{bmatrix}, \quad \begin{bmatrix} -1 & b \\ 0 & 1 \end{bmatrix}.$$

We see therefore that in matrix algebra a quadratic equation may have more than two solutions. This particular equation has, in fact, infinitely many solutions, since b and c are arbitrary.

EXAMPLE 6. Find matrices **X** and **Y** such that **AX**=**B** and **YA**=**B** where

$$\mathbf{A} = \begin{bmatrix} 2 & -1 \\ -3 & 2 \end{bmatrix}, \quad \mathbf{B} = \begin{bmatrix} 3 & 2 \\ -6 & -5 \end{bmatrix}.$$

Now

$$\mathbf{A}^{-1} = \begin{bmatrix} 2 & 1 \\ 3 & 2 \end{bmatrix}.$$

Multiplying the equation **AX**=**B** by $\mathbf{A}^{-1}$ on the left we obtain

$$\mathbf{A}^{-1}\mathbf{A}\mathbf{X} = \mathbf{A}^{-1}\mathbf{B},$$

or
$$\mathbf{X} = \mathbf{A}^{-1}\mathbf{B} = \begin{bmatrix} 2 & 1 \\ 3 & 2 \end{bmatrix}\begin{bmatrix} 3 & 2 \\ -6 & -5 \end{bmatrix} = \begin{bmatrix} 0 & -1 \\ -3 & -4 \end{bmatrix}.$$

Similarly, multiplying the equation **YA**=**B** by $\mathbf{A}^{-1}$ on the right we obtain

$$\mathbf{Y} = \mathbf{B}\mathbf{A}^{-1} = \begin{bmatrix} 3 & 2 \\ -6 & -5 \end{bmatrix}\begin{bmatrix} 2 & 1 \\ 3 & 2 \end{bmatrix} = \begin{bmatrix} 12 & 7 \\ -27 & -16 \end{bmatrix}.$$

EXAMPLE 7. If the matrix **A** is given by

$$\mathbf{A} = \begin{bmatrix} -2 & -9 \\ 1 & 4 \end{bmatrix} \quad \text{prove that} \quad \mathbf{A}^n = \begin{bmatrix} 1-3n & -9n \\ n & 1+3n \end{bmatrix},$$

where n is a positive integer. This result is most easily proved by the method of induction. We see by inspection that the result certainly holds if $n=1$. Assume that it holds for $n=k$. Then

$$\mathbf{A}^{k+1} = \mathbf{A}^k.\mathbf{A} = \begin{bmatrix} 1-3k & -9k \\ k & 1+3k \end{bmatrix}\begin{bmatrix} -2 & -9 \\ 1 & 4 \end{bmatrix}$$

$$= \begin{bmatrix} -2-3k & -9-9k \\ k+1 & 4+3k \end{bmatrix} = \begin{bmatrix} 1-3(k+1) & -9(k+1) \\ k+1 & 1+3(k+1) \end{bmatrix}.$$

Thus if the result is true for $n=k$ it is also true for $n=k+1$. But it is true for $n=1$, and therefore it is true for $n=2, 3, \ldots$, i.e., it is true for any positive integer.

Examples 1

1. Given that **AB**=**BA**, where **A** is a diagonal but not a scalar matrix, prove that **B** is diagonal.

2. If $\mathbf{J} = \begin{bmatrix} 0 & 0 & 1 \\ 0 & 1 & 0 \\ 1 & 0 & 0 \end{bmatrix}$ prove that $\mathbf{J}^2 = \mathbf{1}$.

3. Solve the equations

$$\begin{aligned} x + y + 2z &= 4, \\ 3x - y - z &= 2, \\ 2x + 5y + 3z &= 3. \end{aligned}$$

4. Find matrices $\mathbf{X}$ and $\mathbf{Y}$ such that $\mathbf{AX} = \mathbf{B}$ and $\mathbf{YA} = \mathbf{B}$, where

$$\mathbf{A} = \begin{bmatrix} 2 & -1 \\ -2 & 3 \end{bmatrix}, \quad \mathbf{B} = \begin{bmatrix} 7 & 6 \\ 9 & 8 \end{bmatrix}.$$

5. Find all the 2×2 matrices $\mathbf{X}$ satisfying the equation

$$\mathbf{X}^2 + 3\mathbf{X} + 2\mathbf{1} = \mathbf{0}.$$

6. If $\mathbf{B} = \begin{bmatrix} 11 & -25 \\ 4 & -9 \end{bmatrix}$, prove that $\mathbf{B}^n = \begin{bmatrix} 1+10n & -25n \\ 4n & 1-10n \end{bmatrix}$, where n is a positive integer.

CHAPTER 2

Linear Equations, Linear Dependence and Some Special Types of Matrices

IN Chapter 1 we considered the solution of a set of linear equations of the form $\mathbf{AX}=\mathbf{B}$, where $\mathbf{A}$ is square and the vector $\mathbf{B}$ is not the zero vector. Such a set of equations is said to be *non-homogeneous.* We now consider the special case when $\mathbf{B}=\mathbf{0}$. The equations now have the form $\mathbf{AX}=\mathbf{0}$, and such a set of equations is said to be *homogeneous.*

2·1 Solution of a set of *n* homogeneous linear equations in *n* unknowns

If $\mathbf{A}$ is a square matrix of order n and $\mathbf{X}$ is a column vector of order n, the matrix equation $\mathbf{AX}=\mathbf{0}$ is equivalent to a set of n homogeneous linear equations in the n unknowns $x_1, x_2, \ldots, x_n$. Clearly the equations are satisfied if $x_1=x_2=\cdots=x_n=0$, that is, if $\mathbf{X}=\mathbf{0}$, for any matrix $\mathbf{A}$. This solution is called *trivial.* We are interested in *non-trivial* solutions, when they exist. Such solutions do not always exist. For example the equations

$$x_1 - x_2 = 0,$$

$$x_1 + 2x_2 = 0$$

have $x_1=x_2=0$ as their only solution. Moreover, if a non-trivial solution does exist, it is not unique. For suppose $\mathbf{X}\neq\mathbf{0}$ satisfies the equation $\mathbf{AX}=\mathbf{0}$. Then if k is any scalar

$$\mathbf{A}(k\mathbf{X}) = k(\mathbf{AX}) = k.\mathbf{0} = \mathbf{0},$$

so that $k\mathbf{X}$ is also a solution. The existence of non-trivial solutions will clearly depend on the matrix $\mathbf{A}$. We now prove the following theorem.

Theorem I. *If* $\mathbf{A}$ *is a matrix of order* $n\times n$ *and* $\mathbf{X}$ *a column vector, the equations* $\mathbf{AX}=\mathbf{0}$ *have a non-trivial solution if, and only if,* $|\mathbf{A}|=0$.

First let us suppose that $|\mathbf{A}|\neq 0$ and $\mathbf{AX}=\mathbf{0}$. Then $\mathbf{A}^{-1}$ exists, so that

$$\mathbf{A}^{-1}(\mathbf{AX}) = \mathbf{0}.$$

But $$\mathbf{A}^{-1}(\mathbf{AX}) = (\mathbf{A}^{-1}\mathbf{A})\mathbf{X} = \mathbf{1X} = \mathbf{X}.$$

Hence $\mathbf{X} = \mathbf{0}.$

Consequently if $|\mathbf{A}| \neq 0$, the equations $\mathbf{AX} = \mathbf{0}$ have only the trivial solution $\mathbf{X} = \mathbf{0}$.

Now suppose that $|\mathbf{A}| = 0$. We prove, by the method of induction, that the equations $\mathbf{AX} = \mathbf{0}$ have a non-trivial solution.

$\mathbf{A}$ is an $n \times n$ matrix with $|\mathbf{A}| = 0$.

If $n = 1$ the matrix equation is equivalent to the single equation

$$a_{11}x_1 = 0, \quad \text{with} \quad |\mathbf{A}| = a_{11} = 0.$$

This is satisfied by all values of x_1, so that the equation has a non-trivial solution and the result is certainly true in this case.

Now assume that the result is true for $n = k-1$ $(k \geqslant 2)$; that is, we assume that,

> if $\mathbf{B}$ is a $(k-1) \times (k-1)$ matrix with $|\mathbf{B}| = 0$ and $\mathbf{Y}$ a column vector of order $k-1$, then the equations $\mathbf{BY} = \mathbf{0}$ have a non-trivial solution. (7)

Consider the equations $\mathbf{AX} = \mathbf{0}$, where $\mathbf{A}$ is of order $k \times k$ and $|\mathbf{A}| = 0$. If all the elements in the last column of $\mathbf{A}$ are equal to zero, then clearly $\mathbf{X} = \{0 \;\; 0 \;\; \ldots \;\; 0 \;\; 1\}$ satisfies the equation $\mathbf{AX} = \mathbf{0}$ and we have found a non-trivial solution. If at least one element in the last column does not vanish, we may suppose without loss of generality that this element is a_{kk}, simply by rearranging the order in which the k equations are written if necessary. Thus $a_{kk} \neq 0$. From the ith row $(i = 1, 2, \ldots, k-1)$ of the determinant $|\mathbf{A}|$ we now subtract a_{ik}/a_{kk} times the kth row. This does not alter the value of the determinant. Thus

$$|\mathbf{A}| = \begin{vmatrix} a_{11} & a_{12} & \ldots & a_{1k} \\ a_{21} & a_{22} & \ldots & a_{2k} \\ \cdot & \cdot & \cdot & \cdot \\ a_{k1} & a_{k2} & \ldots & a_{kk} \end{vmatrix}$$

$$= \begin{vmatrix} a_{11} - \dfrac{a_{1k}}{a_{kk}} a_{k1} & a_{12} - \dfrac{a_{1k}}{a_{kk}} a_{k2} & \ldots & 0 \\ a_{21} - \dfrac{a_{2k}}{a_{kk}} a_{k1} & a_{22} - \dfrac{a_{2k}}{a_{kk}} a_{k2} & \ldots & 0 \\ \cdot & \cdot & \cdot & \cdot \\ a_{k1} & a_{k2} & \ldots & a_{kk} \end{vmatrix}$$

$$= \begin{vmatrix} b_{11} & b_{12} & \dots & b_{1,k-1} & 0 \\ b_{21} & b_{22} & \dots & b_{2,k-1} & 0 \\ \cdot & \cdot & \cdot & \cdot & \cdot \\ b_{k-1,1} & b_{k-1,2} & \dots & b_{k-1,k-1} & 0 \\ a_{k,1} & a_{k,2} & \dots & a_{k,k-1} & a_{kk} \end{vmatrix}$$

where $$b_{ih} = a_{ih} - \frac{a_{ik}}{a_{kk}} a_{kh} \quad (i, h = 1, 2, \dots, k-1).$$

Expanding this determinant by its last column we obtain $|\mathbf{A}| = a_{kk}|\mathbf{B}|$, where $\mathbf{B}$ is a $(k-1)\times(k-1)$ matrix. But $|\mathbf{A}|=0$ and $a_{kk}\neq 0$, so that $|\mathbf{B}|=0$.

It follows from our assumption (7) that the equations $\mathbf{BY}=\mathbf{0}$ have a non-trivial solution; i.e. there exists a vector

$$\mathbf{Y}^{(k-1)} = \{y_1 \quad y_2 \quad \dots \quad y_{k-1}\}$$

not equal to the zero vector such that $\mathbf{BY}=\mathbf{0}$. We therefore have

$$\sum_{h=1}^{k-1} b_{ih} y_h = 0, \quad (i = 1, 2, \dots, k-1),$$

or $$\sum_{h=1}^{k-1} \left(a_{ih} - \frac{a_{ik}}{a_{kk}} a_{kh}\right) y_h = 0.$$

Thus $$\sum_{h=1}^{k-1} a_{ih} y_h = \frac{a_{ik}}{a_{kk}} \sum_{h=1}^{k-1} a_{kh} y_h \quad (i = 1, 2, \dots, k-1). \tag{8}$$

Choose y_k so that $$\sum_{h=1}^{k} a_{kh} y_h = 0, \tag{9}$$

i.e. $$y_k = -\frac{1}{a_{kk}} \sum_{h=1}^{k-1} a_{kh} y_h.$$

Then equation (8) gives $$\sum_{h=1}^{k-1} a_{ih} y_h = -a_{ik} y_k,$$

or $$\sum_{h=1}^{k} a_{ih} y_h = 0 \quad (i = 1, 2, \dots, k-1).$$

These equations, together with equation (9), give

$$\sum_{h=1}^{k} a_{ih} y_h = 0 \quad (i = 1, 2, \dots, k)$$

or $$\mathbf{AY} = \mathbf{0}.$$

Moreover $\mathbf{Y}$ is not the zero vector.

We have thus shown that if the result stated in (7) is true for $k-1$ equations, then it is also true for k equations. But it is true for 1 equation, and is therefore true for 2, 3, ..., equations, i.e. it is true for any finite number n of equations by induction.

We have shown that if $|\mathbf{A}|\neq 0$, $\mathbf{AX}=\mathbf{0}$ has only the trivial solution $\mathbf{X}=\mathbf{0}$, and if $|\mathbf{A}|=0$, $\mathbf{AX}=\mathbf{0}$ has a non-trivial solution. The theorem is now proved.

2·2 Linear dependence

Let $\mathbf{X}^{(1)}, \mathbf{X}^{(2)}, \ldots, \mathbf{X}^{(p)}$ be a set of vectors all of the same order n. If they satisfy an equation of the form

$$c_1\mathbf{X}^{(1)}+c_2\mathbf{X}^{(2)}+\cdots+c_p\mathbf{X}^{(p)} = \mathbf{0}, \tag{10}$$

where the scalars $c_1, c_2, \ldots, c_p$ are not all zero and the zero on the right of the equation is the zero vector of order n, then the vectors are said to be *linearly dependent*. If, however, equation (10) is satisfied only if $c_1=c_2=\cdots=c_p=0$, then the vectors are said to be *linearly independent*. Let $\mathbf{A}^{(1)}, \mathbf{A}^{(2)}, \ldots, \mathbf{A}^{(n)}$ be the vectors formed by the columns of an $n\times n$ matrix $\mathbf{A}$. Then the equation

$$c_1\mathbf{A}^{(1)}+c_2\mathbf{A}^{(2)}+\cdots+c_n\mathbf{A}^{(n)} = \mathbf{0}$$

is equivalent to the matrix equation

$$\mathbf{AC} = \mathbf{0},$$

where $$\mathbf{C} = \{c_1 \quad c_2 \quad \ldots \quad c_n\}.$$

Now by Theorem I, there exists a vector $\mathbf{C}\neq\mathbf{0}$ satisfying this equation if, and only if, $|\mathbf{A}|=0$.

Thus the columns of $\mathbf{A}$ are linearly dependent if $|\mathbf{A}|=0$ and linearly independent if $|\mathbf{A}|\neq 0$.

Since the rows of $\mathbf{A}$ are the columns of $\mathbf{A}^t$, and since $|\mathbf{A}^t|=|\mathbf{A}|$, it also follows that the rows of $\mathbf{A}$ are linearly dependent if $|\mathbf{A}|=0$ and linearly independent if $|\mathbf{A}|\neq 0$.

We now know that there *do* exist n linearly independent vectors of order n, since the columns of any non-singular $n\times n$ matrix form such a set. In particular the columns of the unit matrix $\mathbf{1}_n$, the so-called *fundamental unit vectors*.

$$\{1\ 0\ 0\ \ldots\ 0\},\quad \{0\ 1\ 0\ \ldots\ 0\},\quad \ldots,\quad \{0\ 0\ 0\ \ldots\ 0\ 1\}$$

are linearly independent. If we denote these vectors by $\mathbf{E}^{(1)}, \mathbf{E}^{(2)}, \ldots, \mathbf{E}^{(n)}$ we can express any vector $\mathbf{Y} = \{y_1 \quad y_2 \quad \ldots \quad y_n\}$ in the form

$$\mathbf{Y} = y_1\mathbf{E}^{(1)}+y_2\mathbf{E}^{(2)}+\cdots+y_n\mathbf{E}^{(n)}$$

so that any n-vector is a linear combination of the n fundamental unit vectors of order n. We can, however, prove the following more general result.

Theorem II. *If* $\mathbf{X}^{(1)}, \mathbf{X}^{(2)}, \ldots, \mathbf{X}^{(n)}$ *are n linearly independent vectors of order n, any non-zero vector* $\mathbf{Y}$ *of order n can be expressed as a linear combination of these vectors.*

Let $\mathbf{X}$ be the matrix whose columns are $\mathbf{X}^{(1)}, \mathbf{X}^{(2)}, \ldots, \mathbf{X}^{(n)}$. By Theorem I, $\mathbf{X}$ is non-singular, i.e. $|\mathbf{X}| \neq 0$ and $\mathbf{X}^{-1}$ exists. Consider the equation

$$\mathbf{XC} = \mathbf{Y}$$

where $\mathbf{C}$ is a vector of order n. Multiplying by $\mathbf{X}^{-1}$ on the left we have

$$\mathbf{X}^{-1}(\mathbf{XC}) = (\mathbf{X}^{-1}\mathbf{X})\mathbf{C} = \mathbf{C} = \mathbf{X}^{-1}\mathbf{Y}.$$

$\mathbf{C}$ is not a zero vector, for if $\mathbf{C} = \mathbf{0}$, then $\mathbf{Y} = \mathbf{XC} = \mathbf{0}$, contrary to hypothesis.

The equation $\mathbf{XC} = \mathbf{Y}$ is equivalent to

$$c_1\mathbf{X}^{(1)} + c_2\mathbf{X}^{(2)} + \cdots + c_n\mathbf{X}^{(n)} = \mathbf{Y},$$

where $c_1, c_2, \ldots, c_n$ are not all zero.

$\mathbf{Y}$ has therefore been expressed as a linear combination of $\mathbf{X}^{(1)}, \mathbf{X}^{(2)}, \ldots, \mathbf{X}^{(n)}$.

This theorem shows that $n+1$ vectors of order n cannot be linearly independent. For suppose, if possible, that the set of $n+1$ vectors $\mathbf{Y}^{(1)}, \mathbf{Y}^{(2)}, \ldots, \mathbf{Y}^{(n+1)}$ of order n is linearly independent. This implies that the set of n vectors $\mathbf{Y}^{(1)}, \mathbf{Y}^{(2)}, \ldots, \mathbf{Y}^{(n)}$ is linearly independent. For if not, then there exist scalars $c_1, c_2, \ldots, c_n$ not all zero, such that

$$c_1\mathbf{Y}^{(1)} + c_2\mathbf{Y}^{(2)} + \cdots + c_n\mathbf{Y}^{(n)} = \mathbf{0}.$$

Therefore

$$c_1\mathbf{Y}^{(1)} + c_2\mathbf{Y}^{(2)} + \cdots + c_n\mathbf{Y}^{(n)} + c_{n+1}\mathbf{Y}^{(n+1)} = \mathbf{0},$$

where $c_{n+1} = 0$, but $c_1, c_2, \ldots, c_n$ are not all zero. This contradicts the assumption that $\mathbf{Y}^{(1)}, \mathbf{Y}^{(2)}, \ldots, \mathbf{Y}^{(n)}, \mathbf{Y}^{(n+1)}$ are linearly independent. By Theorem II we can express the vector $\mathbf{Y}^{(n+1)}$ as a linear combination of the n linearly independent vectors $\mathbf{Y}^{(1)}, \mathbf{Y}^{(2)}, \ldots, \mathbf{Y}^{(n)}$. That is to say we can find a set of constants $k_1, k_2, \ldots, k_n$ not all zero, such that

$$\mathbf{Y}^{(n+1)} = k_1\mathbf{Y}^{(1)} + k_2\mathbf{Y}^{(2)} + \cdots + k_n\mathbf{Y}^{(n)},$$

or

$$k_1\mathbf{Y}^{(1)} + k_2\mathbf{Y}^{(2)} + \cdots + k_n\mathbf{Y}^{(n)} - \mathbf{Y}^{(n+1)} = \mathbf{0}.$$

This contradicts our original hypothesis that

$$\mathbf{Y}^{(1)}, \mathbf{Y}^{(2)}, \ldots, \mathbf{Y}^{(n)}, \mathbf{Y}^{(n+1)}$$

are linearly independent and this hypothesis is therefore false.

EXAMPLE 8. Show that the vectors $\mathbf{X}^{(1)}=\{1 \quad 2 \quad 3\}$, $\mathbf{X}^{(2)}=\{-1 \quad 2 \quad 4\}$, and $\mathbf{X}^{(3)}=\{1 \quad 6 \quad -5\}$ are linearly independent and express the vector $\mathbf{Y}=\{2 \quad 16 \quad 12\}$ as a linear combination of $\mathbf{X}^{(1)}, \mathbf{X}^{(2)}, \mathbf{X}^{(3)}$.

$$|\mathbf{X}| = \begin{vmatrix} 1 & -1 & 1 \\ 2 & 2 & 6 \\ 3 & 4 & -5 \end{vmatrix} = \begin{vmatrix} 1 & 0 & 0 \\ 2 & 4 & 4 \\ 3 & 7 & -8 \end{vmatrix} = -60 \neq 0.$$

The three vectors $\mathbf{X}^{(1)}, \mathbf{X}^{(2)}, \mathbf{X}^{(3)}$ are therefore linearly independent, since they are the columns of the matrix $\mathbf{X}$, and moreover

$$\mathbf{X}^{-1} = -\frac{1}{60}\begin{bmatrix} -34 & -1 & -8 \\ 28 & -8 & -4 \\ 2 & -7 & 4 \end{bmatrix} = \frac{1}{60}\begin{bmatrix} 34 & 1 & 8 \\ -28 & 8 & 4 \\ -2 & 7 & -4 \end{bmatrix}.$$

If $\mathbf{XC}=\mathbf{Y}$, then

$$\mathbf{C} = \mathbf{X}^{-1}\mathbf{Y} = \frac{1}{60}\begin{bmatrix} 34 & 1 & 8 \\ -28 & 8 & 4 \\ -2 & 7 & -4 \end{bmatrix}\begin{bmatrix} 2 \\ 16 \\ 12 \end{bmatrix}$$

$$= \frac{1}{60}\begin{bmatrix} 180 \\ 120 \\ 60 \end{bmatrix} = \begin{bmatrix} 3 \\ 2 \\ 1 \end{bmatrix}.$$

Hence $$\mathbf{Y} = 3\mathbf{X}^{(1)}+2\mathbf{X}^{(2)}+\mathbf{X}^{(1)}.$$

2·3 Symmetric and Hermitian matrices

In physics we frequently encounter certain special types of matrices. Some of these will now be defined. If $\mathbf{A}^t=\mathbf{A}$, the matrix $\mathbf{A}$ is said to be *symmetric*. This implies that $\mathbf{A}$ is square and $a_{ik}=a_{ki}$. The matrix is therefore symmetrical about its leading diagonal. Clearly $\mathbf{A}^{-1}$, if it exists, is also symmetric. For $\mathbf{A}^{-1}\mathbf{A}=\mathbf{1}$ gives, on transposing,

$$\mathbf{A}^t(\mathbf{A}^{-1})^t = \mathbf{A}(\mathbf{A}^{-1})^t = \mathbf{1},$$

so that $(\mathbf{A}^{-1})^t=\mathbf{A}^{-1}$.

EXAMPLE 9. The equation $ax^2+2hxy+by^2=1$, representing a conic section with respect to rectangular cartesian coordinates may be written in the form

$$[x \quad y]\begin{bmatrix} a & h \\ h & b \end{bmatrix}\begin{bmatrix} x \\ y \end{bmatrix} = 1,$$

or

$$\mathbf{X}^t\mathbf{A}\mathbf{X} = 1,$$

where $\mathbf{X}$ is the column vector $\{x \quad y\}$ and $\mathbf{A}$ is the symmetric matrix

$$\begin{bmatrix} a & h \\ h & b \end{bmatrix}.$$

The reader may be interested to note that the equation of the tangent to the conic at the point (x_1, y_1) is $\mathbf{X}^t\mathbf{A}\mathbf{X}^{(1)}=1$, where $\mathbf{X}^{(1)}=\{x_1 \quad y_1\}$.

Similarly the quadric with rectangular cartesian equation

$$ax^2+by^2+cz^2+2fyz+2gzx+2hxy = 1$$

has a matrix equation of the form

$$\mathbf{X}^t\mathbf{A}\mathbf{X} = 1,$$

where $\mathbf{X}=\{x \quad y \quad z\}$ and the symmetric matrix $\mathbf{A}$ is given by

$$\mathbf{A} = \begin{bmatrix} a & h & g \\ h & b & f \\ g & f & c \end{bmatrix}.$$

Again the tangent plane to the quadric at the point (x_1, y_1, z_1) has equation $\mathbf{X}^t\mathbf{A}\mathbf{X}^{(1)}=1$, where $\mathbf{X}^{(1)}=\{x_1 \quad y_1 \quad z_1\}$.

If $\mathbf{A}^t=-\mathbf{A}$ the matrix $\mathbf{A}$ is said to be *skew-symmetric*. $\mathbf{A}$ is square and $a_{ik}=-a_{ki}$. When $k=i$ this gives $a_{ii}=-a_{ii}$, so that $a_{ii}=0$ for each i. The leading diagonal therefore consists entirely of zero elements.

The elements of a matrix are not necessarily real numbers. We have already had an example in §1·3 of a matrix whose elements are complex numbers. The matrix obtained from a given matrix $\mathbf{A}$ by replacing each element a_{ik} by its complex conjugate $\bar{a}_{ik}$ is called the *conjugate* of $\mathbf{A}$ and denoted by $\bar{\mathbf{A}}$. Clearly $(\bar{\mathbf{A}})^t=\overline{(\mathbf{A}^t)}$ and $\bar{\bar{\mathbf{A}}}=\mathbf{A}$.

If $\bar{\mathbf{A}}^t=\mathbf{A}$ the matrix $\mathbf{A}$ is said to be *Hermitian*. If $\mathbf{A}$ is real, $\bar{\mathbf{A}}=\mathbf{A}$, so that a real Hermitian matrix is symmetric.

If $\bar{\mathbf{A}}^t=-\mathbf{A}$, $\mathbf{A}$ is said to be *skew-Hermitian*. A real skew-Hermitian matrix is skew-symmetric.

2·4 Orthogonal matrices

Let (x_1, x_2) be the rectangular cartesian coordinates of a point P in a plane. The axes are now rotated about the origin O through an angle θ

in the positive (counter-clockwise) sense and the new coordinates of P are (y_1, y_2). It is well-known that

$$y_1 = x_1 \cos\theta + x_2 \sin\theta,$$

$$y_2 = -x_1 \sin\theta + x_2 \cos\theta.$$

In matrix form this can be written

$$\mathbf{Y} = \mathbf{AX}, \quad \text{where} \quad \mathbf{A} = \begin{bmatrix} \cos\theta & \sin\theta \\ -\sin\theta & \cos\theta \end{bmatrix}.$$

Now $\mathbf{AA}^t = \begin{bmatrix} \cos\theta & \sin\theta \\ -\sin\theta & \cos\theta \end{bmatrix} \begin{bmatrix} \cos\theta & -\sin\theta \\ \sin\theta & \cos\theta \end{bmatrix} = \begin{bmatrix} 1 & 0 \\ 0 & 1 \end{bmatrix} = \mathbf{1},$

so that $\mathbf{A}^t = \mathbf{A}^{-1}.$

This matrix, which corresponds to a transformation of coordinates from one set of orthogonal (i.e., perpendicular) axes to another, is called an *orthogonal* matrix. We can regard the transformation from another point of view. The length OP is unaltered by the change of axes, and

$$OP^2 = x_1^2 + x_2^2 = y_1^2 + y_2^2,$$

or $\mathbf{X}^t\mathbf{X} = [x_1 \quad x_2] \begin{bmatrix} x_1 \\ x_2 \end{bmatrix} = x_1^2 + x_2^2 = \mathbf{Y}^t\mathbf{Y}.$

But $\mathbf{Y}^t\mathbf{Y} = (\mathbf{AX})^t(\mathbf{AX}) = (\mathbf{X}^t\mathbf{A}^t)(\mathbf{AX}) = \mathbf{X}^t(\mathbf{A}^t\mathbf{A})\mathbf{X}$

and $\mathbf{X}^t(\mathbf{A}^t\mathbf{A})\mathbf{X} = \mathbf{X}^t\mathbf{X}$ for every $\mathbf{X}$ if, and only if, $\mathbf{A}^t\mathbf{A} = \mathbf{1}$.

Let us consider the same problem in three dimensions. The point P has rectangular cartesian coordinates (x_1, x_2, x_3). The axes are rotated about the origin, which is fixed, in such a way that they remain rectangular, and P has coordinates (y_1, y_2, y_3) referred to the new axes. If (l_1, m_1, n_1), (l_2, m_2, n_2), (l_3, m_3, n_3) are the direction cosines of the new axes referred to the old, it is well-known that

$$y_1 = l_1x_1 + m_1x_2 + n_1x_3,$$

$$y_2 = l_2x_1 + m_2x_2 + n_2x_3,$$

$$y_3 = l_3x_1 + m_3x_2 + n_3x_3.$$

In matrix form this is

$$\mathbf{Y} = \mathbf{AX}, \quad \text{where} \quad \mathbf{A} = \begin{bmatrix} l_1 & m_1 & n_1 \\ l_2 & m_2 & n_2 \\ l_3 & m_3 & n_3 \end{bmatrix}.$$

Again $$\mathbf{X}^t\mathbf{X} = OP^2 = \mathbf{Y}^t\mathbf{Y} = \mathbf{X}^t(\mathbf{A}^t\mathbf{A})\mathbf{X},$$

and this holds for all $\mathbf{X}$ if, and only if, $\mathbf{A}^t\mathbf{A}=\mathbf{1}$, i.e.

$$\begin{bmatrix} l_1 & l_2 & l_3 \\ m_1 & m_2 & m_3 \\ n_1 & n_2 & n_3 \end{bmatrix}\begin{bmatrix} l_1 & m_1 & n_1 \\ l_2 & m_2 & n_2 \\ l_3 & m_3 & n_3 \end{bmatrix} = \begin{bmatrix} 1 & 0 & 0 \\ 0 & 1 & 0 \\ 0 & 0 & 1 \end{bmatrix}.$$

The reader will see that this is equivalent to the six familiar relations

$$l_1^2+l_2^2+l_3^2 = 1, \qquad m_1^2+m_2^2+m_3^2 = 1, \qquad n_1^2+n_2^2+n_3^2 = 1,$$

$$l_1m_1+l_2m_2+l_3m_3 = 0, \qquad m_1n_1+m_2n_2+m_3n_3 = 0,$$

$$n_1l_1+n_2l_2+n_3l_3 = 0.$$

It is convenient to use the same geometrical language to describe the above algebraic process when the order of the vectors involved is greater than 3. Let $\mathbf{X}=\{x_1 \ \ x_2 \ \ \ldots \ \ x_n\}$ be a real column vector, so that x_i is real for each i. We may regard the elements $x_1, x_2, \ldots, x_n$ as the rectangular cartesian coordinates of a point P in a space of n dimensions, in which

$$\mathbf{X}^t\mathbf{X} = x_1^2+x_2^2+\cdots+x_n^2$$

defines the squared length of the vector OP. Now suppose that the axes are rotated rigidly about O to a new position and that the coordinates of P with respect to the new axes are $(y_1, y_2, \ldots, y_n)$, where $\mathbf{Y}=\mathbf{AX}$, $\mathbf{A}$ being an $n\times n$ matrix. Let us suppose, moreover, that the length of the vector OP is unaltered by this transformation. Then, as before,

$$\mathbf{X}^t\mathbf{X} = \mathbf{Y}^t\mathbf{Y} = \mathbf{X}^t(\mathbf{A}^t\mathbf{A})\mathbf{X}$$

for every vector $\mathbf{X}$, and this is true if, and only if, $\mathbf{A}^t\mathbf{A}=\mathbf{1}$.

We are thus led to the following definition:

A real square matrix $\mathbf{A}$ for which $\mathbf{A}^t\mathbf{A}=\mathbf{1}$ (or $\mathbf{A}^{-1}=\mathbf{A}^t$) is called an *orthogonal matrix.*

If the points P, Q in three dimensional space have rectangular cartesian coordinates (x_1, x_2, x_3), (y_1, y_2, y_3), it is well-known that OP is perpendicular (i.e. orthogonal) to OQ if, and only if,

$$x_1y_1+x_2y_2+x_3y_3 = 0.$$

The left-hand side is, in fact, equal to $OP.OQ \cos \angle POQ$. We generalise this result by analogy. The vectors

$$\mathbf{X}=\{x_1 \ \ x_2 \ \ \ldots \ \ x_n\} \ \text{ and } \ \mathbf{Y} = \{y_1 \ \ y_2 \ \ \ldots \ \ y_n\}$$

are said to be orthogonal if

$$\mathbf{X}^t\mathbf{Y} = x_1y_1+x_2y_2+\cdots+x_ny_n = 0,$$

i.e. if their inner product is zero.

The reader should verify that the square matrix **A** is orthogonal if, and only if, the length of each of its column vectors is 1 and each column is orthogonal to every other column. If **A** is orthogonal, $\mathbf{A}^t$ is obviously also orthogonal, so that the rows of **A** (which are the columns of $\mathbf{A}^t$) have these properties also. Moreover

$$|\mathbf{1}| = |\mathbf{A}^t\mathbf{A}| = |\mathbf{A}^t|.|\mathbf{A}| = |\mathbf{A}|^2 = 1$$

so that
$$|\mathbf{A}| = \pm 1.$$

These definitions may be generalised to the case when a matrix has complex elements. If **X** is a column vector whose elements are complex numbers, then

$$\mathbf{X}^t\mathbf{X} = x_1^2+x_2^2+\cdots+x_n^2$$

is no longer necessarily real and is not a suitable definition of the squared length of the vector **X**. However

$$\bar{\mathbf{X}}^t\mathbf{X} = \bar{x}_1x_1+\bar{x}_2x_2+\cdots+\bar{x}_nx_n$$
$$= |x_1|^2+|x_2|^2+\cdots+|x_n|^2.$$

This is always real, and we take this as the definition of the squared length of **X** in this case. Note that, if **X** is real, $\bar{\mathbf{X}}=\mathbf{X}$, so that $\bar{\mathbf{X}}^t\mathbf{X}=\mathbf{X}^t\mathbf{X}$ and our previous definition is therefore included in this one. If $\mathbf{Y}=\mathbf{AX}$ we now have

$$\bar{\mathbf{Y}}^t\mathbf{Y} = (\overline{\mathbf{AX}})^t(\mathbf{AX}) = (\bar{\mathbf{X}}^t\bar{\mathbf{A}}^t)(\mathbf{AX}) = \bar{\mathbf{X}}^t(\bar{\mathbf{A}}^t\mathbf{A})\mathbf{X}$$

so that $\bar{\mathbf{Y}}^t\mathbf{Y}=\bar{\mathbf{X}}^t\mathbf{X}$ for all **X** if, and only if, $\bar{\mathbf{A}}^t\mathbf{A}=\mathbf{1}$.

A square matrix **A** for which $\bar{\mathbf{A}}^t\mathbf{A}=\mathbf{1}$ is called a *unitary matrix*. A real unitary matrix is clearly orthogonal.

2·5 Partitioned matrices

We can sometimes simplify calculations involving matrices if we partition them into submatrices. Let **A** be an $m\times n$ matrix and $q<n$ a positive integer. Imagine a vertical line drawn between columns q and $q+1$. The first q columns of **A** may be regarded as forming a matrix of order $m\times q$ and the last $n-q$ columns as forming a matrix of

order $m\times(n-q)$. Denoting these two matrices by $\mathbf{A}_1$, $\mathbf{A}_2$ respectively, we write

$$\mathbf{A} = \left[\begin{array}{cccc|ccc} a_{11} & a_{12} & \cdots & a_{1q} & a_{1,q+1} & \cdots & a_{1n} \\ a_{21} & a_{22} & \cdots & a_{2q} & a_{2,q+1} & \cdots & a_{2n} \\ \cdot & \cdot & \cdot & \cdot & \cdot & \cdot & \cdot \\ a_{m1} & a_{m2} & \cdots & a_{mq} & a_{m,q+1} & \cdots & a_{mn} \end{array}\right] = [\mathbf{A}_1 \quad \mathbf{A}_2].$$

Consider the equation $\mathbf{AX}=\mathbf{Y}$, where $\mathbf{X}$ and $\mathbf{Y}$ are both column vectors of order n. Then

$$y_i = (a_{i1}x_1+a_{i2}x_2+\cdots+a_{iq}x_q)+(a_{i,q+1}x_{q+1}+\cdots+a_{in}x_n). \quad (11)$$

Let the column vector $\mathbf{X}$ be partitioned by supposing a horizontal line drawn between its qth and $(q+1)$th elements. Thus

$$\mathbf{X} = \begin{bmatrix}\mathbf{X}_1\\ \mathbf{X}_2\end{bmatrix}, \quad \text{say,}$$

where $\mathbf{X}_1$ may be regarded as a column vector of order q and $\mathbf{X}_2$ a column vector of order $n-q$. Equation (11) may now be written

$$y_i = i\text{th element of } \mathbf{A}_1\mathbf{X}_1 + i\text{th element of } \mathbf{A}_2\mathbf{X}_2$$

so that

$$\mathbf{Y} = \mathbf{A}_1\mathbf{X}_1+\mathbf{A}_2\mathbf{X}_2 = [\mathbf{A}_1 \quad \mathbf{A}_2]\begin{bmatrix}\mathbf{X}_1\\ \mathbf{X}_2\end{bmatrix}. \quad (12)$$

We can therefore multiply matrices partitioned in this way as though the submatrices were themselves elements of a matrix. Now $\mathbf{AX}$ exists only if the number of columns of $\mathbf{A}$ is equal to the number of rows of $\mathbf{X}$, and the product can be formed as in equation (12) if, and only if, the partitioning of $\mathbf{A}$ by columns is exactly the same as the partitioning of $\mathbf{X}$ by rows. Thus if we divide $\mathbf{A}$ into the first q and the remaining $n-q$ columns we must divide $\mathbf{X}$ into the first q and the remaining $n-q$ rows. We can also partition $\mathbf{A}$ by rows, say by dividing it into the first p and the remaining $m-p$ rows. $\mathbf{A}$ is then partitioned into four submatrices as follows:

$$\mathbf{A} = \begin{bmatrix}\mathbf{A}_{11} & \mathbf{A}_{12}\\ \mathbf{A}_{21} & \mathbf{A}_{22}\end{bmatrix}$$

where $\mathbf{A}_{11}$, $\mathbf{A}_{12}$, $\mathbf{A}_{21}$, $\mathbf{A}_{22}$ are of orders $p\times q$, $p\times(n-q)$, $(m-p)\times q$, $(m-p)\times(n-q)$ respectively. It is easily seen that

$$[\mathbf{A}_{11} \quad \mathbf{A}_{12}]\begin{bmatrix}\mathbf{X}_1\\ \mathbf{X}_2\end{bmatrix} = \mathbf{A}_{11}\mathbf{X}_1+\mathbf{A}_{12}\mathbf{X}_2 = \mathbf{Y}_1$$

is a column vector consisting of the first p elements of **Y**, and

$$[\mathbf{A}_{21} \quad \mathbf{A}_{22}] \begin{bmatrix} \mathbf{X}_1 \\ \mathbf{X}_2 \end{bmatrix} = \mathbf{A}_{21}\mathbf{X}_1 + \mathbf{A}_{22}\mathbf{X}_2 = \mathbf{Y}_2$$

is a column vector consisting of the last $m-p$ elements of **Y**. Hence if we partition **Y** by rows, exactly as **A** is partitioned by rows, writing $\mathbf{Y} = \begin{bmatrix} \mathbf{Y}_1 \\ \mathbf{Y}_2 \end{bmatrix}$, we have

$$\begin{bmatrix} \mathbf{A}_{11} & \mathbf{A}_{12} \\ \mathbf{A}_{21} & \mathbf{A}_{22} \end{bmatrix} \begin{bmatrix} \mathbf{X}_1 \\ \mathbf{X}_2 \end{bmatrix} = \begin{bmatrix} \mathbf{Y}_1 \\ \mathbf{Y}_2 \end{bmatrix}.$$

This equation may be interpreted as though each submatrix were an element of a matrix.

More generally, consider a matrix equation

$$\mathbf{AB} = \mathbf{C}$$

where **A**, **B**, **C** are of orders $m \times n$, $n \times s$, $m \times s$ respectively. We can partition **A**, **B**, **C** as follows:

$$\begin{bmatrix} \mathbf{A}_{11} & \mathbf{A}_{12} \\ \mathbf{A}_{21} & \mathbf{A}_{22} \end{bmatrix} \begin{bmatrix} \mathbf{B}_{11} & \mathbf{B}_{12} \\ \mathbf{B}_{21} & \mathbf{B}_{22} \end{bmatrix} = \begin{bmatrix} \mathbf{C}_{11} & \mathbf{C}_{12} \\ \mathbf{C}_{21} & \mathbf{C}_{22} \end{bmatrix}.$$

A is partitioned by columns and **B** is partitioned by rows in the same way. The row partitioning of **C** is the same as the row partitioning of **A**, and the column partitioning of **C** is the same as the column partitioning of **B**. In these circumstances the partitioning is said to be *conformable* and we have

$$\mathbf{C}_{11} = \mathbf{A}_{11}\mathbf{B}_{11} + \mathbf{A}_{12}\mathbf{B}_{21},$$

$$\mathbf{C}_{12} = \mathbf{A}_{11}\mathbf{B}_{12} + \mathbf{A}_{12}\mathbf{B}_{22},$$

$$\mathbf{C}_{21} = \mathbf{A}_{21}\mathbf{B}_{11} + \mathbf{A}_{22}\mathbf{B}_{21},$$

$$\mathbf{C}_{22} = \mathbf{A}_{21}\mathbf{B}_{12} + \mathbf{A}_{22}\mathbf{B}_{22}.$$

These are precisely the rules for multiplication that would apply if $\mathbf{A}_{11}$, $\mathbf{A}_{12}$, etc. were elements instead of submatrices.

We can, of course, partition a matrix into any number of submatrices.

E.g.

$$\mathbf{A} = \left[\begin{array}{c:c:c} \mathbf{A}_{11} & \mathbf{A}_{12} & \mathbf{A}_{13} \\ \hdashline \mathbf{A}_{21} & \mathbf{A}_{22} & \mathbf{A}_{23} \end{array}\right].$$

The calculation of reciprocals can be laborious for matrices of high order and in some cases we can simplify the process using partitioned matrices. The reciprocal of a non-singular 2×2 matrix can be written down by inspection.

$$\begin{bmatrix} a & b \\ c & d \end{bmatrix}^{-1} = \frac{1}{ad-cb}\begin{bmatrix} d & -b \\ -c & a \end{bmatrix}.$$

Consider a 4×4 non-singular matrix $\mathbf{A}$, partitioned into four 2×2 matrices so that

$$\mathbf{A} = \begin{bmatrix} \mathbf{A}_1 & \mathbf{A}_2 \\ \mathbf{A}_3 & \mathbf{A}_4 \end{bmatrix}.$$

Suppose further that $\mathbf{A}_2 = \mathbf{0}$, the zero matrix of order 2×2. Now $|\mathbf{A}| = |\mathbf{A}_1| . |\mathbf{A}_4|$, so that $\mathbf{A}_1$ and $\mathbf{A}_4$ are both non-singular and $\mathbf{A}_1^{-1}$, $\mathbf{A}_4^{-1}$ exist and can be written down by inspection. Let $\mathbf{A}^{-1} = \mathbf{B}$ also be partitioned in the same way as $\mathbf{A}$, so that

$$\begin{bmatrix} \mathbf{A}_1 & \mathbf{0} \\ \mathbf{A}_3 & \mathbf{A}_4 \end{bmatrix}\begin{bmatrix} \mathbf{B}_1 & \mathbf{B}_2 \\ \mathbf{B}_3 & \mathbf{B}_4 \end{bmatrix} = \begin{bmatrix} \mathbf{1} & \mathbf{0} \\ \mathbf{0} & \mathbf{1} \end{bmatrix}$$

where each $\mathbf{1}$ and each $\mathbf{0}$ on the right-hand side is a 2×2 matrix. Then

$$\mathbf{A}_1\mathbf{B}_1 = \mathbf{1} \quad \text{so that} \quad \mathbf{B}_1 = \mathbf{A}_1^{-1}.$$

$$\mathbf{A}_1\mathbf{B}_2 = \mathbf{0} \quad \text{and} \quad |\mathbf{A}_1| \neq 0 \quad \text{so that} \quad \mathbf{B}_2 = \mathbf{0}.$$

$$\mathbf{A}_3\mathbf{B}_1 + \mathbf{A}_4\mathbf{B}_3 = \mathbf{0} \quad \text{and} \quad \mathbf{A}_4\mathbf{B}_4 = \mathbf{1}.$$

Hence $\qquad \mathbf{B}_4 = \mathbf{A}_4^{-1}, \qquad \mathbf{B}_3 = -\mathbf{A}_4^{-1}\mathbf{A}_3\mathbf{A}_1^{-1}.$

We then have
$$\begin{bmatrix} \mathbf{A}_1 & \mathbf{0} \\ \mathbf{A}_3 & \mathbf{A}_4 \end{bmatrix}^{-1} = \begin{bmatrix} \mathbf{A}_1^{-1} & \mathbf{0} \\ -\mathbf{A}_4^{-1}\mathbf{A}_3\mathbf{A}_1^{-1} & \mathbf{A}_4^{-1} \end{bmatrix},$$

the only calculation being the evaluation of the product of three 2×2 matrices.

Example 10. Find the reciprocal of the matrix

$$\begin{bmatrix} 1 & 1 & 0 & 0 \\ 1 & 2 & 0 & 0 \\ 5 & 2 & 3 & -1 \\ -1 & 1 & -5 & 2 \end{bmatrix}.$$

In this case

$$\mathbf{A}_1 = \begin{bmatrix} 1 & 1 \\ 1 & 2 \end{bmatrix}, \qquad \mathbf{A}_1^{-1} = \begin{bmatrix} 2 & -1 \\ -1 & 1 \end{bmatrix}.$$

$$\mathbf{A}_4 = \begin{bmatrix} 3 & -1 \\ -5 & 2 \end{bmatrix}, \quad \mathbf{A}_4^{-1} = \begin{bmatrix} 2 & 1 \\ 5 & 3 \end{bmatrix}.$$

$$-\mathbf{A}_4^{-1}\mathbf{A}_3\mathbf{A}_1^{-1} = \begin{bmatrix} -2 & -1 \\ -5 & -3 \end{bmatrix} \begin{bmatrix} 5 & 2 \\ -1 & 1 \end{bmatrix} \begin{bmatrix} 2 & -1 \\ -1 & 1 \end{bmatrix}$$

$$= \begin{bmatrix} -9 & -5 \\ -22 & -13 \end{bmatrix} \begin{bmatrix} 2 & -1 \\ -1 & 1 \end{bmatrix}$$

$$= \begin{bmatrix} -13 & 4 \\ -31 & 9 \end{bmatrix}.$$

The required reciprocal is therefore

$$\begin{bmatrix} 2 & -1 & 0 & 0 \\ -1 & 1 & 0 & 0 \\ -13 & 4 & 2 & 1 \\ -31 & 9 & 5 & 3 \end{bmatrix}.$$

Examples 2

1. Show that the vectors $\mathbf{X}^{(1)}=\{1 \quad 2 \quad 3\}$, $\mathbf{X}^{(2)}=\{-1 \quad 6 \quad 4\}$ and $\mathbf{X}^{(3)}=\{1 \quad -2 \quad -2\}$ are linearly independent and express the vector $\mathbf{Y}=\{2 \quad 8 \quad 5\}$ as a linear combination of $\mathbf{X}^{(1)}$, $\mathbf{X}^{(2)}$, $\mathbf{X}^{(3)}$.

2. Show that the matrix

$$\begin{bmatrix} 1/\sqrt{2} & -1/\sqrt{3} & 1/\sqrt{6} \\ 0 & 1/\sqrt{3} & 2/\sqrt{6} \\ 1/\sqrt{2} & 1/\sqrt{3} & -1/\sqrt{6} \end{bmatrix}$$

is orthogonal.

3. By suitable partitioning, or otherwise, find the reciprocal of the matrix

$$\begin{bmatrix} -1 & 1 & 0 & 0 \\ -5 & 4 & 0 & 0 \\ 2 & 3 & 1 & -1 \\ 6 & 1 & -2 & 3 \end{bmatrix}.$$

4. The equation of a conic referred to rectangular cartesian coordinates is

$$13x^2 - 10xy + 13y^2 = 72.$$

Write this equation in the form

$$[x \quad y]\mathbf{A}\begin{bmatrix} x \\ y \end{bmatrix} = 72$$

where **A** is a symmetric matrix. Transform this equation by making the substitution

$$\begin{bmatrix} x \\ y \end{bmatrix} = \begin{bmatrix} 1/\sqrt{2} & 1/\sqrt{2} \\ -1/\sqrt{2} & 1/\sqrt{2} \end{bmatrix} \begin{bmatrix} X \\ Y \end{bmatrix}.$$

Show that the matrix of this transformation is orthogonal and hence show that the given conic is an ellipse with semi-axes 2 and 3.

CHAPTER 3

Transformation to Diagonal Form

THE algebra of diagonal matrices is very simple. We have already seen that two diagonal matrices of the same order commute and it follows that the product of any finite number of diagonal matrices of the same order is independent of the order in which the factors occur. Moreover the product matrix is also diagonal and each diagonal element is the product of the corresponding elements of the factors. As a special case of this result we have the following:

If $$\mathbf{\Lambda} = \begin{bmatrix} \lambda_1 & 0 & \dots & 0 \\ 0 & \lambda_2 & \dots & 0 \\ \cdot & \cdot & \cdot & \cdot \\ 0 & 0 & \dots & \lambda_n \end{bmatrix}$$

is a diagonal matrix and p is a positive integer

$$\mathbf{\Lambda}^p = \begin{bmatrix} \lambda_1^p & 0 & \dots & 0 \\ 0 & \lambda_2^p & \dots & 0 \\ \cdot & \cdot & \cdot & \cdot \\ 0 & 0 & \dots & \lambda_n^p \end{bmatrix}.$$

We can obviously greatly simplify our calculations if we can find a method of transforming a given matrix to diagonal form and we now show how this can be done for a large class of matrices.

3·1 The eigenvalues of a matrix

If $\mathbf{X}=\{x_1 \quad x_2 \quad x_3\}$ is a real vector in three dimensions, the vector $\lambda\mathbf{X}=\{\lambda x_1 \quad \lambda x_2 \quad \lambda x_3\}$, where λ is any real scalar, represents a vector having the same direction as $\mathbf{X}$. By analogy we say that, if $\mathbf{X}$ is a vector of any order n and λ is any scalar, then the vectors $\lambda\mathbf{X}$ and $\mathbf{X}$ have the same direction.

Let $\mathbf{A}$ be a square $n \times n$ matrix and consider the equation

$$\mathbf{AX} = \lambda\mathbf{X}$$

where λ is a scalar, and $\mathbf{X}$ is a vector of order n. Then $\mathbf{AX}$ is also a vector of order n and we may regard it as the result of applying to the vector $\mathbf{X}$ a transformation defined by the matrix $\mathbf{A}$. The equation

$$\mathbf{AX} = \lambda\mathbf{X}$$

therefore poses the following question. Are there any directions (defined by the vector $\mathbf{X}$) that are left invariant (i.e. unchanged) by the transformation defined by $\mathbf{A}$? The equation may be written in the form

$$\mathbf{AX} = \lambda\mathbf{1X} \quad (\text{where } \mathbf{1} = \mathbf{1}_n)$$

or

$$(\mathbf{A}-\lambda\mathbf{1})\mathbf{X} = \mathbf{0}. \tag{13}$$

Now $\mathbf{A}-\lambda\mathbf{1}$ is a square matrix (of order $n\times n$) and, by Theorem I, equation (13) has a non-trivial solution $\mathbf{X}$ if, and only if, $|\mathbf{A}-\lambda\mathbf{1}|=0$. λ must therefore satisfy the equation

$$\begin{vmatrix} a_{11}-\lambda & a_{12} & \dots & a_{1n} \\ a_{21} & a_{22}-\lambda & \dots & a_{2n} \\ \cdot & \cdot & \cdot & \cdot \\ a_{n1} & a_{n2} & \dots & a_{nn}-\lambda \end{vmatrix} = 0,$$

which is clearly of degree n in λ. The terms in λ^n and λ^{n-1} occur only in the product of all the terms in the leading diagonal. The term independent of λ is obtained by putting $\lambda=0$ in the determinant and is therefore equal to $|\mathbf{A}|$. Multiplying by $(-1)^n$, the equation for λ consequently has the form

$$\lambda^n-(a_{11}+a_{22}+\cdots+a_{nn})\lambda^{n-1}+\cdots+(-1)^n|\mathbf{A}| = 0.$$

The sum of the elements in the leading diagonal of a matrix is called the *trace* of the matrix (abbreviated to tr) so that

$$\lambda^n-(\text{tr }\mathbf{A})\lambda^{n-1}+\cdots+(-1)^n|\mathbf{A}| = 0. \tag{14}$$

Equation (14) is called the *characteristic equation* of the matrix $\mathbf{A}$. The roots of this equation are called the *eigenvalues* (or latent roots, or characteristic roots) of the matrix $\mathbf{A}$. Now an equation of degree n has n roots. These roots need not all be distinct and they may be real or complex. If the coefficients are all real, complex roots occur in conjugate pairs. Let the eigenvalues of $\mathbf{A}$ be $\lambda_1, \lambda_2, \dots, \lambda_n$. Then equation (14) may be written

$$(\lambda-\lambda_1)(\lambda-\lambda_2)\dots(\lambda-\lambda_n) = 0. \tag{15}$$

It is easily seen that the coefficient of λ^{n-1} in this equation is $-(\lambda_1+\lambda_2+\cdots+\lambda_n)$, so that on comparing this with equation (14) we see that

$$\lambda_1+\lambda_2+\cdots+\lambda_n = \text{tr }\mathbf{A}.$$

Again, the term independent of λ in equation (15) is $(-1)^n\lambda_1\lambda_2\ldots\lambda_n$ and this must be equal to $(-1)^n|\mathbf{A}|$. We therefore have the following result:

The sum of the eigenvalues of a matrix **A** *is* tr **A** *and the product of the eigenvalues is* $|\mathbf{A}|$. Hence if **A** is non-singular none of its eigenvalues is equal to zero, and vice versa.

Corresponding to each eigenvalue λ there exists a non-zero column vector **X** satisfying the equation $\mathbf{AX}=\lambda\mathbf{X}$. **X** is known as the (column) *eigenvector* (latent column vector, characteristic vector, pole) corresponding to the eigenvalue λ. If **X** satisfies the equation, clearly any scalar multiple $k\mathbf{X}$ of **X** also satisfies it. If

$$|\mathbf{A}-\lambda\mathbf{1}| = 0,$$

then

$$|(\mathbf{A}-\lambda\mathbf{1})^t| = 0,$$

or

$$|\mathbf{A}^t-\lambda\mathbf{1}^t| = |\mathbf{A}^t-\lambda\mathbf{1}| = 0,$$

so that λ is also an eigenvalue of $\mathbf{A}^t$, and **A** and $\mathbf{A}^t$ have the same eigenvalues. Hence if λ is an eigenvalue of **A** there exists a non-zero column vector **Y** satisfying

$$\mathbf{A}^t\mathbf{Y} = \lambda\mathbf{Y}.$$

Transposing this equation we obtain

$$\mathbf{Y}^t\mathbf{A} = \lambda\mathbf{Y}^t.$$

$\mathbf{Y}^t$ is called the *row eigenvector* of **A** corresponding to the eigenvalue λ. Henceforward in this book we shall use the term eigenvector to mean column eigenvector and we shall specify "row" or "column" only when both kinds are involved and it is necessary in order to avoid ambiguity.

EXAMPLE 11. Find the eigenvalues and the corresponding eigenvectors of the matrix

$$\mathbf{A} = \begin{bmatrix} 2 & 1 & 1 \\ 2 & 3 & 4 \\ -1 & -1 & -2 \end{bmatrix}.$$

The eigenvalues λ are given by the characteristic equation

$$\begin{vmatrix} 2-\lambda & 1 & 1 \\ 2 & 3-\lambda & 4 \\ -1 & -1 & -2-\lambda \end{vmatrix} = 0.$$

Subtracting the second column from the first and the third column from the second we have

$$\begin{vmatrix} 1-\lambda & 0 & 1 \\ -1+\lambda & -1-\lambda & 4 \\ 0 & 1+\lambda & -2-\lambda \end{vmatrix} = 0.$$

This gives

$$(1-\lambda)(1+\lambda)\begin{vmatrix} 1 & 0 & 1 \\ -1 & -1 & 4 \\ 0 & 1 & -2-\lambda \end{vmatrix} = 0,$$

$$(1-\lambda)(1+\lambda)(2+\lambda-4-1) = 0,$$

$$(1-\lambda)(1+\lambda)(\lambda-3) = 0.$$

Thus $\lambda=1, -1, 3$.

When $\lambda=1$ the equations $\mathbf{AX}=\lambda\mathbf{X}$, or $(\mathbf{A}-\lambda\mathbf{1})\mathbf{X}=\mathbf{0}$, become

$$\begin{aligned} x_1+\ x_2+\ x_3 &= 0, \\ 2x_1+2x_2+4x_3 &= 0, \\ -x_1-\ x_2-3x_3 &= 0. \end{aligned}$$

All solutions satisfy the equations $x_1+x_2=0$, $x_3=0$. Thus $\{1 \quad -1 \quad 0\}$ is an eigenvector corresponding to the eigenvalue 1 and all others are of the form $k\{1 \quad -1 \quad 0\}$ where k is a scalar.

When $\lambda=-1$ the equations become

$$\begin{aligned} 3x_1+\ x_2+\ x_3 &= 0, \\ 2x_1+4x_2+4x_3 &= 0, \\ -x_1-\ x_2-\ x_3 &= 0. \end{aligned}$$

$x_1=x_2+x_3=0$ satisfies these equations, so that $\{0 \quad 1 \quad -1\}$ is an eigenvector corresponding to the eigenvalue -1.

When $\lambda=3$ the equations become

$$\begin{aligned} -x_1+x_2+\ x_3 &= 0, \\ 2x_1 \qquad +4x_3 &= 0, \\ -x_1-x_2-5x_3 &= 0. \end{aligned}$$

$3x_1=2x_2=-6x_3$ satisfies these equations, so that $\{2 \quad 3 \quad -1\}$ is an eigenvector corresponding to the eigenvalue 3.

These three eigenvectors are linearly independent. For if $\mathbf{Q}$ is the 3×3 matrix having them as its columns, then

$$|\mathbf{Q}| = \begin{vmatrix} 1 & 0 & 2 \\ -1 & 1 & 3 \\ 0 & -1 & -1 \end{vmatrix} = 2+2 \neq 0.$$

This is a special case of a more general theorem.

3·2 Linear independence of the eigenvectors

Theorem III. *If the eigenvalues of a matrix* $\mathbf{A}$ *are all distinct, then the eigenvectors are linearly independent.*

Let $\lambda_1, \lambda_2, \ldots, \lambda_n$ be the eigenvalues of the $n\times n$ matrix $\mathbf{A}$, where $\lambda_i \neq \lambda_k$ $(i\neq k)$, and let $\mathbf{Q}^{(k)}$ be the eigenvector corresponding to the eigenvalue λ_k. Then

$$\mathbf{A}\mathbf{Q}^{(k)} = \lambda_k\mathbf{Q}^{(k)} \quad (k = 1, 2, \ldots, n).$$

Hence
$$\mathbf{A}^2\mathbf{Q}^{(k)} = \mathbf{A}(\mathbf{A}\mathbf{Q}^{(k)}) = \mathbf{A}(\lambda_k\mathbf{Q}^{(k)}) = \lambda_k\mathbf{A}\mathbf{Q}^{(k)}$$
$$= \lambda_k.\lambda_k\mathbf{Q}^{(k)} = \lambda_k^2\mathbf{Q}^{(k)}.$$

By the method of induction we can show that $\mathbf{A}^p\mathbf{Q}^{(k)} = \lambda_k^p\mathbf{Q}^k$ for any positive integer p.

Let
$$\mathbf{Y} = c_1\mathbf{Q}^{(1)}+c_2\mathbf{Q}^{(2)}+\cdots+c_n\mathbf{Q}^{(n)} = \mathbf{0},$$

where $c_1, c_2, \ldots, c_n$ are scalars. We now show that c_k must be zero for every k.

If p is any positive integer

$$\mathbf{A}^p\mathbf{Y} = \mathbf{A}^p(c_1\mathbf{Q}^{(1)}+c_2\mathbf{Q}^{(2)}+\cdots+c_n\mathbf{Q}^{(n)})$$
$$= c_1\mathbf{A}^p\mathbf{Q}^{(1)}+c_2\mathbf{A}^p\mathbf{Q}^{(2)}+\cdots+c_n\mathbf{A}^p\mathbf{Q}^{(n)}$$
$$= c_1\lambda_1^p\mathbf{Q}^{(1)}+c_2\lambda_2^p\mathbf{Q}^{(2)}+\cdots+c_n\lambda_n^p\mathbf{Q}^{(n)}.$$

But since $\mathbf{Y}=\mathbf{0}$, $\mathbf{A}^p\mathbf{Y}=\mathbf{0}$.

Thus the kth element of each of the vectors $\mathbf{Y}, \mathbf{A}\mathbf{Y}, \mathbf{A}^2\mathbf{Y}, \ldots, \mathbf{A}^{n-1}\mathbf{Y}$ is zero. This gives us the following set of n equations in the n unknowns $c_1q_k^{(1)}, c_2q_k^{(2)}, \ldots, c_nq_k^{(n)}$:

$$\begin{aligned} c_1q_k^{(1)}+ \quad c_2q_k^{(2)}+\cdots+ \quad c_nq_k^{(n)} &= 0, \\ \lambda_1c_1q_k^{(1)}+ \quad \lambda_2c_2q_k^{(2)}+\cdots+ \quad \lambda_nc_nq_k^{(n)} &= 0, \\ \lambda_1^2c_1q_k^{(1)}+ \quad \lambda_2^2c_2q_k^{(2)}+\cdots+ \quad \lambda_n^2c_nq_k^{(n)} &= 0, \\ \cdots\cdots\cdots\cdots\cdots\cdots & \\ \lambda_1^{n-1}c_1q_k^{(1)}+\lambda_2^{n-1}c_2q_k^{(2)}+\cdots+\lambda_n^{n-1}c_nq_k^{(n)} &= 0. \end{aligned} \tag{16}$$

By Theorem I, these equations have a non-trivial solution if, and only if,

$$\begin{vmatrix} 1 & 1 & 1 & \dots & 1 \\ \lambda_1 & \lambda_2 & \lambda_3 & \dots & \lambda_n \\ \lambda_1^2 & \lambda_2^2 & \lambda_3^2 & \dots & \lambda_n^2 \\ \cdot & \cdot & \cdot & \cdot & \cdot \\ \lambda_1^{n-1} & \lambda_2^{n-1} & \lambda_3^{n-1} & \dots & \lambda_n^{n-1} \end{vmatrix} = 0,$$

i.e.

$$\prod_{i>k}(\lambda_i - \lambda_k) = 0.$$

The left-hand side denotes the product of all factors of the form $\lambda_i - \lambda_k$ with $i>k$, $i \leqslant n$, $k<n$. But none of the factors $\lambda_i - \lambda_k$ is zero, by hypothesis, so that their product cannot vanish. Hence the equations (16) have only the trivial solution

$$c_1 q_k^{(1)} = c_2 q_k^{(2)} = \dots = c_n q_k^{(n)} = 0.$$

This is true for $k = 1, 2, \dots, n$, so that

$$c_1 \mathbf{Q}^{(1)} = c_2 \mathbf{Q}^{(2)} = \dots = c_n \mathbf{Q}^{(n)} = \mathbf{0}.$$

But the vectors $\mathbf{Q}^{(1)}, \mathbf{Q}^{(2)}, \dots, \mathbf{Q}^{(n)}$ are all eigenvectors and are consequently not zero vectors. Hence

$$c_1 = c_2 = \dots = c_n = 0.$$

We have thus shown that if

$$c_1 \mathbf{Q}^{(1)} + c_2 \mathbf{Q}^{(2)} + \dots + c_n \mathbf{Q}^{(n)} = \mathbf{0},$$

then

$$c_1 = c_2 = \dots = c_n = 0.$$

The vectors $\mathbf{Q}^{(1)}, \mathbf{Q}^{(2)}, \dots, \mathbf{Q}^{(n)}$ are therefore linearly independent and the theorem is proved.

The condition $\lambda_i \neq \lambda_k$ if $i \neq k$ is a sufficient but not a necessary condition for the eigenvectors to be linearly independent. It does not necessarily follow that, if the eigenvalues of an $n \times n$ matrix are not all distinct, the matrix does *not* possess n linearly independent eigenvectors. We shall illustrate this by means of an example.

EXAMPLE 12. Let $\mathbf{A}$ be the matrix

$$\begin{bmatrix} 2 & 1 & 1 \\ 2 & 3 & 2 \\ 3 & 3 & 4 \end{bmatrix}.$$

The eigenvalues are the roots of the equation

$$\begin{vmatrix} 2-\lambda & 1 & 1 \\ 2 & 3-\lambda & 2 \\ 3 & 3 & 4-\lambda \end{vmatrix} = 0,$$

i.e.
$$(1-\lambda)^2(7-\lambda) = 0.$$

Consequently $\lambda=1$, 1, 7 and the eigenvalues are not distinct. When $\lambda=7$ the equations $\mathbf{AX}=\lambda\mathbf{X}$ become

$$-5x_1+\ x_2+\ x_3 = 0,$$
$$2x_1-4x_2+2x_3 = 0,$$
$$3x_1+3x_2-3x_3 = 0.$$

$\mathbf{X}=\{1\ \ 2\ \ 3\}$ is a solution and all others are scalar multiples of this.

When $\lambda=1$ the equations $\mathbf{AX}=\lambda\mathbf{X}$ all become

$$x_1+x_2+x_3 = 0.$$

$\mathbf{X}=\{1\ \ 0\ \ -1\}$ and $\mathbf{X}=\{0\ \ 1\ \ -1\}$ are both solutions, and these are linearly independent since neither is a scalar multiple of the other. Moreover every eigenvector corresponding to the eigenvalue 1 is a linear combination of these two. For every eigenvector is of the form $\{\alpha\ \ \beta\ \ -(\alpha+\beta)\}$ and we may write

$$\{\alpha\ \ \beta\ \ -(\alpha+\beta)\} = \alpha\{1\ \ 0\ \ -1\}+\beta\{0\ \ 1\ \ -1\}.$$

There are therefore precisely two linearly independent eigenvectors corresponding to the eigenvector 1.

The three eigenvectors $\{1\ \ 2\ \ 3\}$, $\{1\ \ 0\ \ -1\}$, $\{0\ \ 1\ \ -1\}$ are linearly independent, since

$$\begin{vmatrix} 1 & 0 & 1 \\ 0 & 1 & 2 \\ -1 & -1 & 3 \end{vmatrix} = \begin{vmatrix} 1 & 0 & 1 \\ 0 & 1 & 2 \\ 0 & -1 & 4 \end{vmatrix} = 6 \neq 0.$$

The three eigenvalues of this matrix are not distinct but the matrix *does* possess three linearly independent eigenvectors. This is not, however, always true when the characteristic equation has multiple roots.

3·3 Reduction to diagonal canonical form

We now prove the main theorem of this section. We show first how to transform to diagonal form a matrix whose eigenvalues are distinct and then show how to extend the result to matrices of the type considered in Example 12.

Theorem IV. *If* $\mathbf{A}$ *is a non-singular square matrix with distinct eigenvalues, then there exists a non-singular matrix* $\mathbf{Q}$ *of the same order such that the product* $\mathbf{Q}^{-1}\mathbf{A}\mathbf{Q}$ *is a diagonal matrix.*

Let $\mathbf{A}$ be of order $n \times n$ and let $\lambda_1, \lambda_2, \ldots, \lambda_n$ be its eigenvalues and $\mathbf{Q}^{(1)}, \mathbf{Q}^{(2)}, \ldots, \mathbf{Q}^{(n)}$ be the corresponding eigenvectors.

By Theorem III these eigenvectors are linearly independent, so that $\mathbf{Q}$, the matrix whose columns are $\mathbf{Q}^{(1)}, \mathbf{Q}^{(2)}, \ldots, \mathbf{Q}^{(n)}$, is non-singular and consequently $\mathbf{Q}^{-1}$ exists. Now

$$\mathbf{A}\mathbf{Q}^{(1)} = \lambda_1 \mathbf{Q}^{(1)}, \qquad \mathbf{A}\mathbf{Q}^{(2)} = \lambda_2 \mathbf{Q}^{(2)}, \ldots, \qquad \mathbf{A}\mathbf{Q}^{(n)} = \lambda_n \mathbf{Q}^{(n)}.$$

The reader will easily verify that these n equations are equivalent to the single matrix equation

$$\mathbf{A}\mathbf{Q} = \mathbf{Q}\mathbf{\Lambda}$$

where $\mathbf{\Lambda}$ is the $n \times n$ diagonal matrix $\begin{bmatrix} \lambda_1 & 0 & \ldots & 0 \\ 0 & \lambda_2 & \ldots & 0 \\ \cdot & \cdot & \cdot & \cdot \\ 0 & 0 & \ldots & \lambda_n \end{bmatrix}$. Multiplying this equation on the left by $\mathbf{Q}^{-1}$ we have

$$\mathbf{Q}^{-1}\mathbf{A}\mathbf{Q} = \mathbf{Q}^{-1}\mathbf{Q}\mathbf{\Lambda} = \mathbf{\Lambda}.$$

We say that by means of the transformation $\mathbf{Q}^{-1}\mathbf{A}\mathbf{Q}$ we have reduced the matrix $\mathbf{A}$ to *diagonal canonical form* $\mathbf{\Lambda}$. Note that the order in which the eigenvalues occur in $\mathbf{\Lambda}$ is the same as the order in which the corresponding column eigenvectors occur in $\mathbf{Q}$.

EXAMPLE 13. Reduce to diagonal form the matrix

$$\mathbf{A} = \begin{bmatrix} 2 & 1 & 1 \\ 2 & 3 & 4 \\ -1 & -1 & -2 \end{bmatrix}.$$

In Example 11 we proved that this matrix has eigenvalues $1, -1, 3$ with corresponding eigenvectors $\{1 \ \ -1 \ \ 0\}$, $\{0 \ \ 1 \ \ -1\}$, $\{2 \ \ 3 \ \ -1\}$. Hence in this case

$$\mathbf{Q} = \begin{bmatrix} 1 & 0 & 2 \\ -1 & 1 & 3 \\ 0 & -1 & -1 \end{bmatrix}, \qquad \mathbf{Q}^{-1} = \frac{1}{4}\begin{bmatrix} 2 & -2 & -2 \\ -1 & -1 & -5 \\ 1 & 1 & 1 \end{bmatrix},$$

since $|\mathbf{Q}|$ was shown in Example 11 to be equal to 4,

$$\mathbf{Q}^{-1}\mathbf{A}\mathbf{Q} = \frac{1}{4}\begin{bmatrix} 2 & -2 & -2 \\ -1 & -1 & -5 \\ 1 & 1 & 1 \end{bmatrix}\begin{bmatrix} 2 & 1 & 1 \\ 2 & 3 & 4 \\ -1 & -1 & -2 \end{bmatrix}\begin{bmatrix} 1 & 0 & 2 \\ -1 & 1 & 3 \\ 0 & -1 & -1 \end{bmatrix}$$

$$= \frac{1}{4}\begin{bmatrix} 2 & -2 & -2 \\ -1 & -1 & -5 \\ 1 & 1 & 1 \end{bmatrix}\begin{bmatrix} 1 & 0 & 6 \\ -1 & -1 & 9 \\ 0 & 1 & -3 \end{bmatrix}$$

$$= \frac{1}{4}\begin{bmatrix} 4 & 0 & 0 \\ 0 & -4 & 0 \\ 0 & 0 & 12 \end{bmatrix} = \begin{bmatrix} 1 & 0 & 0 \\ 0 & -1 & 0 \\ 0 & 0 & 3 \end{bmatrix},$$

i.e. $\mathbf{Q}^{-1}\mathbf{A}\mathbf{Q}=\mathbf{\Lambda}$.

The proof of Theorem IV depended only on the fact that the eigenvectors $\mathbf{Q}^{(1)}, \mathbf{Q}^{(2)}, \ldots, \mathbf{Q}^{(n)}$ were linearly independent. This, by Theorem III, is always the case when the eigenvalues are distinct. We have seen, however, that there may be n linearly independent eigenvectors even when the eigenvalues are not distinct (cf. Example 12). It can be proved that the number of linearly independent eigenvectors of an $n \times n$ matrix never exceeds n, though it can be less than n. The reader should satisfy himself that when this number is equal to n, the proof of Theorem IV remains valid even when the eigenvalues of the matrix are not all distinct. The theorem could therefore be re-stated as follows:

If $\mathbf{Q}^{(1)}, \mathbf{Q}^{(2)}, \ldots, \mathbf{Q}^{(n)}$ are linearly independent eigenvectors of an $n \times n$ matrix $\mathbf{A}$ and $\mathbf{Q}$ is the (non-singular) matrix having $\mathbf{Q}^{(1)}, \mathbf{Q}^{(2)}, \ldots, \mathbf{Q}^{(n)}$ as its columns, then $\mathbf{Q}^{-1}\mathbf{A}\mathbf{Q}$ is a diagonal matrix.

EXAMPLE 14. Reduce to diagonal form the matrix

$$\mathbf{A} = \begin{bmatrix} 2 & 1 & 1 \\ 2 & 3 & 2 \\ 3 & 3 & 4 \end{bmatrix}.$$

We have shown in Example 12 that this matrix has eigenvalues 1, 1, 7 with corresponding linearly independent eigenvectors $\{1 \;\; 0 \;\; -1\}$, $\{0 \;\; 1 \;\; -1\}$, $\{1 \;\; 2 \;\; 3\}$. In this case,

$$\mathbf{Q} = \begin{bmatrix} 1 & 0 & 1 \\ 0 & 1 & 2 \\ -1 & -1 & 3 \end{bmatrix}, \quad \mathbf{Q}^{-1} = \frac{1}{6}\begin{bmatrix} 5 & -1 & -1 \\ -2 & 4 & -2 \\ 1 & 1 & 1 \end{bmatrix},$$

since $|\mathbf{Q}| = 6$.

$$\mathbf{Q}^{-1}\mathbf{AQ} = \frac{1}{6}\begin{bmatrix} 5 & -1 & -1 \\ -2 & 4 & -2 \\ 1 & 1 & 1 \end{bmatrix}\begin{bmatrix} 2 & 1 & 1 \\ 2 & 3 & 2 \\ 3 & 3 & 4 \end{bmatrix}\begin{bmatrix} 1 & 0 & 1 \\ 0 & 1 & 2 \\ -1 & -1 & 3 \end{bmatrix}$$

$$= \frac{1}{6}\begin{bmatrix} 5 & -1 & -1 \\ -2 & 4 & -2 \\ 1 & 1 & 1 \end{bmatrix}\begin{bmatrix} 1 & 0 & 7 \\ 0 & 1 & 14 \\ -1 & -1 & 21 \end{bmatrix}$$

$$= \frac{1}{6}\begin{bmatrix} 6 & 0 & 0 \\ 0 & 6 & 0 \\ 0 & 0 & 42 \end{bmatrix} = \begin{bmatrix} 1 & 0 & 0 \\ 0 & 1 & 0 \\ 0 & 0 & 7 \end{bmatrix},$$

i.e. $\mathbf{Q}^{-1}\mathbf{AQ} = \mathbf{\Lambda}$.

3·4 Orthogonal reduction to diagonal form

If the matrix **A** of Theorem IV is real and symmetric and has distinct eigenvalues we can choose the matrix **Q** to be orthogonal.

We first note that the eigenvalues of a real symmetric matrix are real.

For if
$$\mathbf{AX} = \lambda\mathbf{X},$$
then
$$\bar{\mathbf{X}}^t\mathbf{AX} = \lambda\bar{\mathbf{X}}^t\mathbf{X}. \tag{17}$$

But $\bar{\mathbf{X}}^t\mathbf{AX}$ and $\bar{\mathbf{X}}^t\mathbf{X}$ are both scalars,

$$\overline{(\bar{\mathbf{X}}^t\mathbf{AX})}^t = \mathbf{X}^t\bar{\mathbf{A}}^t\bar{\mathbf{X}} = \bar{\mathbf{X}}^t\mathbf{AX},$$

since **A** is real and symmetric, and

$$\overline{(\bar{\mathbf{X}}^t\mathbf{X})}^t = \bar{\mathbf{X}}^t\mathbf{X}.$$

It follows that

$$\overline{(\bar{\mathbf{X}}^t\mathbf{AX})} = \bar{\mathbf{X}}^t\mathbf{AX} \quad \text{and} \quad \overline{(\bar{\mathbf{X}}^t\mathbf{X})} = \bar{\mathbf{X}}^t\mathbf{X},$$

since a scalar is unaltered by transposition, and consequently $\bar{\mathbf{X}}^t\mathbf{AX}$ and $\bar{\mathbf{X}}^t\mathbf{X}$ are both real. $\bar{\mathbf{X}}^t\mathbf{X}$ is not zero, since **X** is an eigenvector, and it follows from Equation (17) that λ is real.

Again, since **A** and λ are real, **X** is real. Thus $\mathbf{X}^t\mathbf{X}=x_1^2+x_2^2+\cdots+x_n^2$ is real.

Now $k\mathbf{X}$ is also an eigenvector corresponding to the eigenvalue λ, and if we choose $k=(x_1^2+x_2^2+\cdots+x_n^2)^{-1/2}$, then the vector $k\mathbf{X}$ has unit length. We may therefore choose for every column of the matrix **Q** a vector of length equal to 1.

Now $$\mathbf{AQ}^{(i)} = \lambda_i\mathbf{Q}^{(i)}$$

and transposition gives

$$(\mathbf{Q}^{(i)})^t\mathbf{A}^t = \lambda_i(\mathbf{Q}^{(i)})^t,$$

or $$(\mathbf{Q}^{(i)})^t\mathbf{A} = \lambda_i(\mathbf{Q}^{(i)})^t, \quad \text{since} \quad \mathbf{A}^t = \mathbf{A}.$$

Hence $$(\mathbf{Q}^{(i)})^t\mathbf{AQ}^{(k)} = \lambda_i(\mathbf{Q}^{(i)})^t\mathbf{Q}^{(k)} \quad (i \neq k).$$

But $$(\mathbf{Q}^{(i)})^t\mathbf{AQ}^{(k)} = (\mathbf{Q}^{(i)})^t\lambda_k\mathbf{Q}^{(k)} = \lambda_k(\mathbf{Q}^{(i)})^t\mathbf{Q}^{(k)}.$$

Thus $$(\lambda_i-\lambda_k)(\mathbf{Q}^{(i)})^t\mathbf{Q}^{(k)} = 0$$

and since $$\lambda_i \neq \lambda_k, \quad (\mathbf{Q}^{(i)})^t\mathbf{Q}^{(k)} = 0.$$

The vectors $\mathbf{Q}^{(i)}$ and $\mathbf{Q}^{(k)}$ are therefore orthogonal. This holds for all $i, k=1, 2, \ldots, n$ $(i\neq k)$.

Q is consequently an orthogonal matrix, so that $\mathbf{Q}^{-1}=\mathbf{Q}^t$ and we have

$$\mathbf{Q}^t\mathbf{AQ} = \mathbf{\Lambda}.$$

In this case the calculation of $\mathbf{Q}^{-1}$ which can be troublesome is avoided.

EXAMPLE 15. Find an orthogonal reduction to diagonal form for the matrix

$$\mathbf{A} = \begin{bmatrix} 2 & 1 & 3 \\ 1 & 2 & 3 \\ 3 & 3 & 20 \end{bmatrix}.$$

The eigenvalues are given by

$$\begin{vmatrix} 2-\lambda & 1 & 3 \\ 1 & 2-\lambda & 3 \\ 3 & 3 & 20-\lambda \end{vmatrix} = 0.$$

It is easily verified that they are 1, 2, 21. Thus **A** is a symmetric matrix with distinct eigenvalues and its eigenvectors are consequently orthogonal. They are, in fact, the vectors $\{1 \quad -1 \quad 0\}$, $\{3 \quad 3 \quad -1\}$, $\{1 \quad 1 \quad 6\}$ which are seen to be orthogonal in pairs. For

$$1.3 + -1.3 + 0.-1 = 0,$$
$$3.1 + 3.1 + -1.6 = 0,$$
$$1.1 + -1.1 + 0.6 = 0.$$

The corresponding vectors of unit length are

$$\{1/\sqrt{2} \quad -1/\sqrt{2} \quad 0\}, \qquad \{3/\sqrt{19} \quad 3/\sqrt{19} \quad -1/\sqrt{19}\}, \qquad \{1/\sqrt{38} \quad 1/\sqrt{38} \quad 6/\sqrt{38}\}.$$

We therefore take

$$\mathbf{Q} = \begin{bmatrix} 1/\sqrt{2} & 3/\sqrt{19} & 1/\sqrt{38} \\ -1/\sqrt{2} & 3/\sqrt{19} & 1/\sqrt{38} \\ 0 & -1/\sqrt{19} & 6/\sqrt{38} \end{bmatrix}$$

which is orthogonal. Hence $\mathbf{Q}^{-1} = \mathbf{Q}^t$ and it is easily verified that

$$\mathbf{Q}^t\mathbf{A}\mathbf{Q} = \begin{bmatrix} 1 & 0 & 0 \\ 0 & 2 & 0 \\ 0 & 0 & 21 \end{bmatrix} = \mathbf{\Lambda}.$$

We can interpret this example geometrically. Consider the quadric with rectangular cartesian equation

$$2x^2 + 2y^2 + 20z^2 + 6yz + 6zx + 2xy = 1.$$

This equation may be written in matrix form

$$[x \quad y \quad z] \begin{bmatrix} 2 & 1 & 3 \\ 1 & 2 & 3 \\ 3 & 3 & 20 \end{bmatrix} \begin{bmatrix} x \\ y \\ z \end{bmatrix} = 1.$$

The 3×3 matrix is the matrix **A** of Example 15.

Let us transform to a new set of rectangular axes OX, OY, OZ where

$$\begin{bmatrix} x \\ y \\ z \end{bmatrix} = \mathbf{Q} \begin{bmatrix} X \\ Y \\ Z \end{bmatrix} \quad \text{or} \quad \begin{bmatrix} X \\ Y \\ Z \end{bmatrix} = \mathbf{Q}^t \begin{bmatrix} x \\ y \\ z \end{bmatrix},$$

Q, and hence $\mathbf{Q}^t$ being orthogonal.

Transposing gives $[x \;\; y \;\; z]=[X \;\; Y \;\; Z]\mathbf{Q}^t$. The equation of the quadric now becomes

$$[X \;\; Y \;\; Z]\mathbf{Q}^t\mathbf{A}\mathbf{Q}\begin{bmatrix} X \\ Y \\ Z \end{bmatrix} = 1,$$

i.e.

$$[X \;\; Y \;\; Z]\begin{bmatrix} 1 & 0 & 0 \\ 0 & 2 & 0 \\ 0 & 0 & 21 \end{bmatrix}\begin{bmatrix} X \\ Y \\ Z \end{bmatrix} = 1,$$

or

$$X^2+2Y^2+21Z^2 = 1.$$

This is an ellipsoid whose semi-axes are of lengths 1, $1/\sqrt{2}$, $1/\sqrt{21}$. The principal planes of the ellipsoid are the planes $X=0$, $Y=0$, $Z=0$. But

$$\begin{bmatrix} X \\ Y \\ Z \end{bmatrix} = \begin{bmatrix} 1/\sqrt{2} & -1/\sqrt{2} & 0 \\ 3/\sqrt{19} & 3/\sqrt{19} & -1/\sqrt{19} \\ 1/\sqrt{38} & 1/\sqrt{38} & 6/\sqrt{38} \end{bmatrix}\begin{bmatrix} x \\ y \\ z \end{bmatrix} = \begin{bmatrix} (x-y)/\sqrt{2} \\ (3x+3y-z)/\sqrt{19} \\ (x+y+6z)/\sqrt{38} \end{bmatrix}.$$

Hence, referred to the original axes, the principal planes have equations

$$x-y = 0,$$

$$3x+3y-z = 0,$$

$$x+y+6z = 0.$$

The axes of the ellipsoid are the three lines in which these planes meet in pairs.

3·5 Powers of a matrix

The product $\mathbf{A}.\mathbf{A}$ exists only if $\mathbf{A}$ is square, and we then denote it by $\mathbf{A}^2$, which has the same order as $\mathbf{A}$. $\mathbf{A}^3$ denotes $\mathbf{A}^2.\mathbf{A}$ and by induction we can define $\mathbf{A}^n$ where n is any positive integer. We sometimes have to calculate powers of a square matrix. Multiplication is the simplest method of calculating $\mathbf{A}^n$ if n is small, but it would be laborious to use this method if n is large. It is often better to proceed as in the following example.

EXAMPLE 16. Evaluate $\mathbf{A}^{25}$, where

$$\mathbf{A} = \begin{bmatrix} -1 & 2 \\ 4 & 1 \end{bmatrix}.$$

The eigenvalues of **A** are given by

$$\begin{aligned}(-1-\lambda)(1-\lambda)-8 &= 0,\\ \lambda^2 &= 9,\\ \lambda &= -3, +3.\end{aligned}$$

The corresponding eigenvectors are {1 −1}, {1 2}.

Thus if $\mathbf{Q} = \begin{bmatrix} 1 & 1 \\ -1 & 2 \end{bmatrix}$, $\mathbf{Q}^{-1} = \frac{1}{3}\begin{bmatrix} 2 & -1 \\ 1 & 1 \end{bmatrix}$,

$$\mathbf{Q}^{-1}\mathbf{A}\mathbf{Q} = \begin{bmatrix} -3 & 0 \\ 0 & 3 \end{bmatrix} = \mathbf{\Lambda}.$$

Multiplying on the left by **Q** and on the right by $\mathbf{Q}^{-1}$ gives

$$\mathbf{A} = \mathbf{Q}\mathbf{\Lambda}\mathbf{Q}^{-1}.$$

$$\begin{aligned}\text{Hence } \mathbf{A}^{25} &= (\mathbf{Q\Lambda Q}^{-1})(\mathbf{Q\Lambda Q}^{-1})\ldots(\mathbf{Q\Lambda Q}^{-1}) \quad \text{(25 brackets)}\\ &= \mathbf{Q\Lambda}(\mathbf{Q}^{-1}\mathbf{Q})\mathbf{\Lambda}(\mathbf{Q}^{-1}\mathbf{Q})\mathbf{\Lambda}\ldots\mathbf{\Lambda}(\mathbf{Q}^{-1}\mathbf{Q})\mathbf{\Lambda Q}^{-1} \quad \text{(25 factors } \mathbf{\Lambda})\\ &= \mathbf{Q\Lambda 1\Lambda}\ldots\mathbf{\Lambda 1 \Lambda Q}^{-1}\\ &= \mathbf{Q\Lambda}^{25}\mathbf{Q}^{-1}\\ &= \begin{bmatrix} 1 & 1 \\ -1 & 2 \end{bmatrix}\begin{bmatrix} (-3)^{25} & 0 \\ 0 & 3^{25} \end{bmatrix}\cdot\frac{1}{3}\begin{bmatrix} 2 & -1 \\ 1 & 1 \end{bmatrix}\\ &= 3^{24}\begin{bmatrix} 1 & 1 \\ -1 & 2 \end{bmatrix}\begin{bmatrix} -1 & 0 \\ 0 & 1 \end{bmatrix}\begin{bmatrix} 2 & -1 \\ 1 & 1 \end{bmatrix}\\ &= 3^{24}\begin{bmatrix} 1 & 1 \\ -1 & 2 \end{bmatrix}\begin{bmatrix} -2 & 1 \\ 1 & 1 \end{bmatrix}\\ &= 3^{24}\begin{bmatrix} -1 & 2 \\ 4 & 1 \end{bmatrix}.\end{aligned}$$

Examples 3

1. Find a matrix **Q** such that the matrix $\mathbf{Q}^{-1}\mathbf{A}\mathbf{Q}$ is diagonal, where

$$\mathbf{A} = \begin{bmatrix} 0 & 0 & 1 \\ 0 & 1 & 0 \\ 1 & 0 & 0 \end{bmatrix}.$$

2. Express $\mathbf{A}^n$ in the form of a 2×2 matrix, where n is a positive integer and

$$\mathbf{A} = \begin{bmatrix} 3 & 4 \\ -1 & -2 \end{bmatrix}.$$

3. Find an orthogonal matrix $\mathbf{Q}$ such that $\mathbf{Q}^t\mathbf{A}\mathbf{Q}$ is a diagonal matrix, where

$$\mathbf{A} = \begin{bmatrix} 0 & 2 & 0 \\ 2 & 0 & 0 \\ 0 & 0 & 1 \end{bmatrix}.$$

4. Show that the equation

$$20x^2+9y^2+20z^2+32zx = 36$$

represents an ellipsoid whose semi-axes are of lengths 1, 2, 3 respectively and find the equations of its principal axes.

CHAPTER 4

Four-terminal Networks

IN this and the remaining chapters a number of applications of matrix theory to the solution of various network problems will be given. A typical example is four-terminal network theory.

4·1 The impedance matrix

Consider an n-mesh network in which E_k, I_k are the voltage, current respectively in the kth mesh, the clockwise sense being assumed to be the positive one. It is well-known that the E_k, I_k satisfy a set of n equations of the form

$$E_i = Z_{i1}I_1 + Z_{i2}I_2 + \cdots + Z_{in}I_n = \sum_{k=1}^{n} Z_{ik}I_k \quad (i = 1, 2, \ldots, n)$$

where $Z_{ik} = Z_{ki}$. These may be written in matrix form

$$\mathbf{E} = \mathbf{ZI}$$

where $\mathbf{Z}$ is an $n \times n$ symmetric, non-singular matrix and $\mathbf{E}$, $\mathbf{I}$ are vectors of order n. The matrix $\mathbf{Z}$ is called the *impedance matrix* of the network.

In the particular case of a four-terminal n-mesh passive network all the E_k are zero except two, and there is no loss of generality in supposing that these two are E_1 and E_2. The network considered can therefore be represented as shown in Fig. 1, where the two meshes 1 and 2 are

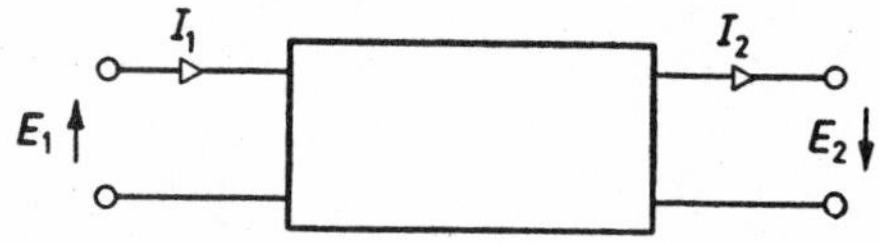

FIG. 1

brought out and the remainder of the network is represented as is customary by a rectangle. Note the sense in which E_1 and E_2 are drawn. This is in accordance with the sign convention introduced above.

Thus $\qquad \mathbf{E} = \mathbf{ZI}, \quad \text{where} \quad E_k = 0 \quad (k > 2).$

Now since **Z** is non-singular and symmetric, $\mathbf{Z}^{-1}$ exists and is also symmetric (cf. §2·3). Hence

$$\mathbf{I} = \mathbf{Z}^{-1}\mathbf{E}.$$

Writing $Z_{ik}^{-1} = Y_{ik}$ $(i, k=1, 2)$, the first two of these equations may be written

$$\begin{aligned} I_1 &= Y_{11}E_1 + Y_{12}E_2, \\ I_2 &= Y_{21}E_1 + Y_{22}E_2, \end{aligned} \tag{18}$$

where $Y_{12} = Y_{21}$.

We have taken the clockwise sense to be positive in every mesh for both E and I. It is, however, more convenient for some applications if we reverse the sense of E_2 as shown in Fig. 2.

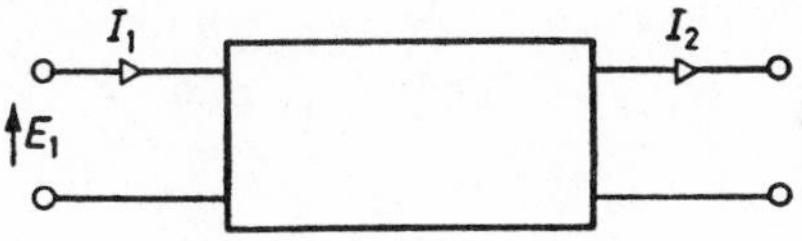

FIG. 2

Equations (18) then become

$$\begin{aligned} I_1 &= Y_{11}E_1 - Y_{12}E_2, \\ I_2 &= Y_{21}E_1 - Y_{22}E_2. \end{aligned} \tag{19}$$

These equations may be written in matrix form

$$\mathbf{I} = \mathbf{YE}.$$

Y is a 2×2 matrix and **I**, **E** are vectors of order 2. I_1, E_1 are the current, voltage respectively at the input end of the four-terminal and I_2, E_2 are the current, voltage respectively at the output end. The equation $\mathbf{I}=\mathbf{YE}$ gives the two currents in terms of the two voltages.

4·2 Parallel connection of four-terminal networks

The matrix **Y** can be used to obtain the resultant matrix of a parallel connection of four-terminal networks.

Fig. 3 illustrates a parallel connection of two four-terminal networks whose matrices corresponding to **Y** of equation (19) are $\mathbf{Y}^{(1)}$ and $\mathbf{Y}^{(2)}$ respectively. With the notation of the figure

$$\begin{bmatrix} I_1' \\ I_2' \end{bmatrix} = \mathbf{Y}^{(1)} \begin{bmatrix} E_1 \\ E_2 \end{bmatrix} \quad \text{and} \quad \begin{bmatrix} I_1'' \\ I_2'' \end{bmatrix} = \mathbf{Y}^{(2)} \begin{bmatrix} E_1 \\ E_2 \end{bmatrix}.$$

But $I_1 = I_1'+I_1''$ and $I_2 = I_2'+I_2''$.

Hence
$$\begin{bmatrix} I_1 \\ I_2 \end{bmatrix} = \begin{bmatrix} I_1' \\ I_2' \end{bmatrix} + \begin{bmatrix} I_1'' \\ I_2'' \end{bmatrix} = \mathbf{Y}^{(1)}\begin{bmatrix} E_1 \\ E_2 \end{bmatrix} + \mathbf{Y}^{(2)}\begin{bmatrix} E_1 \\ E_2 \end{bmatrix},$$

or
$$\begin{bmatrix} I_1 \\ I_2 \end{bmatrix} = (\mathbf{Y}^{(1)}+\mathbf{Y}^{(2)})\begin{bmatrix} E_1 \\ E_2 \end{bmatrix}.$$

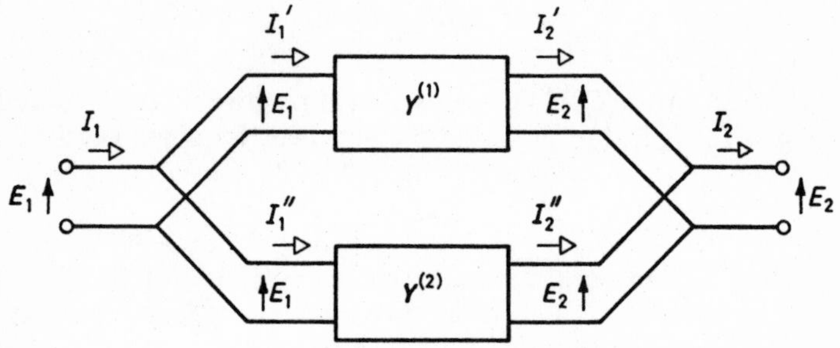

FIG. 3

4·3 Series connection of four-terminal networks

The inverse of the matrix **Y** can be applied in the case of a series connection of four-terminal networks.

Fig. 4 illustrates such a connection of two networks. Let the inverse of the matrix **Y** be **B** so that for any four-terminal network

$$\mathbf{E} = \mathbf{BI}.$$

Let the matrices corresponding to **B** for the two networks shown in Fig. 4 be $\mathbf{B}^{(1)}$ and $\mathbf{B}^{(2)}$ respectively. With the notation of the figure

$$\begin{bmatrix} E_1' \\ E_2' \end{bmatrix} = \mathbf{B}^{(1)}\begin{bmatrix} I_1 \\ I_2 \end{bmatrix} \quad \text{and} \quad \begin{bmatrix} E_1'' \\ E_2'' \end{bmatrix} = \mathbf{B}^{(2)}\begin{bmatrix} I_1 \\ I_2 \end{bmatrix}.$$

But $E_1 = E_1'+E_1''$ and $E_2 = E_2'+E_2''$.

Hence
$$\begin{bmatrix} E_1 \\ E_2 \end{bmatrix} = \begin{bmatrix} E_1' \\ E_2' \end{bmatrix} + \begin{bmatrix} E_1'' \\ E_2'' \end{bmatrix} = (\mathbf{B}^{(1)}+\mathbf{B}^{(2)})\begin{bmatrix} I_1 \\ I_2 \end{bmatrix}.$$

4·4 Cascade connection of four-terminal networks

When dealing with cascade connections we are interested in the relations between the E and I at the input end and the E and I at the output end. We wish therefore to express E_1 and I_1 in terms of E_2 and I_2.

Returning to equations (19) we see that if $Y_{12}=0$ the input voltage and current, E_1 and I_1 are completely independent of the output voltage

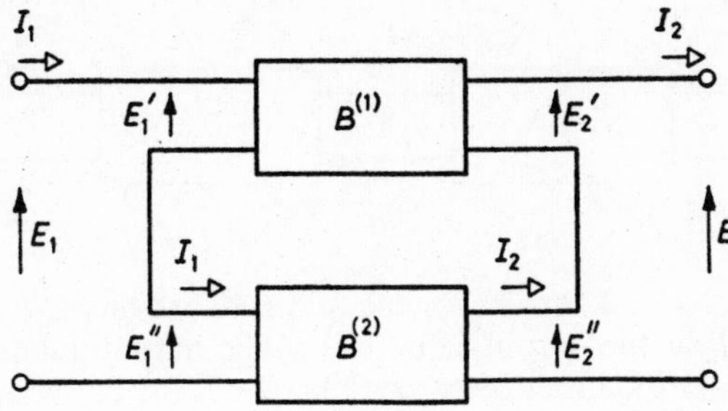

FIG. 4

and current, E_2 and I_2. This would not correspond to the type of network we are considering. We may therefore assume that $Y_{12}\neq 0$ so that equations (19) may be written in the form

$$\begin{aligned} E_1 &= aE_2+bI_2, \\ I_1 &= cE_2+dI_2, \end{aligned} \tag{20}$$

where $a = Y_{22}/Y_{21}, \quad b = 1/Y_{21},$

$$c = (Y_{11}Y_{22}-Y_{12}Y_{21})/Y_{21}, \quad d = Y_{11}/Y_{21}.$$

Remembering that $Y_{12}=Y_{21}$ we can easily verify the important relation

$$ad-bc = 1.$$

Now $ad-bc$ is the determinant of the matrix of equations (20). Hence we can write these equations in the form

$$\begin{bmatrix} E_1 \\ I_1 \end{bmatrix} = \begin{bmatrix} a & b \\ c & d \end{bmatrix} \begin{bmatrix} E_2 \\ I_2 \end{bmatrix} = \mathbf{A}\begin{bmatrix} E_2 \\ I_2 \end{bmatrix}, \tag{21}$$

where the 2×2 matrix $\mathbf{A}$ has determinant 1. We have therefore proved the following result:

With any four-terminal network we can associate a 2×2 *matrix of determinant* 1. Throughout this section we shall refer to this matrix as the matrix of the network.

If we combine two four-terminal networks in cascade we form a single resultant four-terminal network. We wish to find the relationship between the matrix of this resultant and the matrices of the two given networks. Fig. 5 illustrates a cascade connection of two four-terminal networks of matrices **A**, **B** respectively.

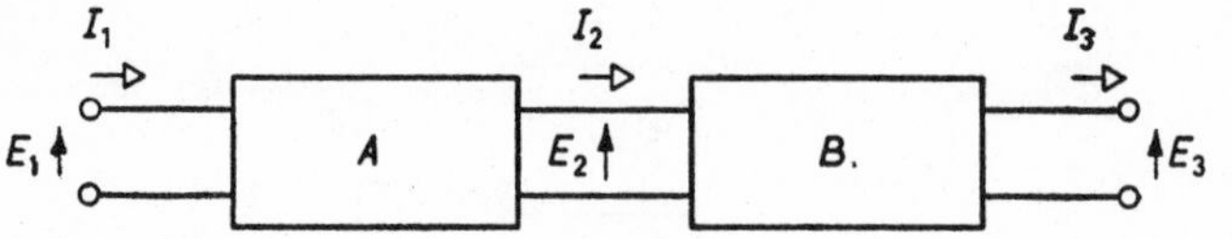

FIG. 5

Let the voltage and current for the first network be E_1, I_1 at the input side and E_2, I_2 at the output side. Since the output quantities for the first network are the input ones for the second, the corresponding voltage and current for the second network are E_2, I_2 at the input side and E_3, I_3 at the output side. Then, as before,

$$\begin{bmatrix} E_1 \\ I_1 \end{bmatrix} = \mathbf{A}\begin{bmatrix} E_2 \\ I_2 \end{bmatrix} \quad \text{and} \quad \begin{bmatrix} E_2 \\ I_2 \end{bmatrix} = \mathbf{B}\begin{bmatrix} E_3 \\ I_3 \end{bmatrix}.$$

Thus

$$\begin{bmatrix} E_1 \\ I_1 \end{bmatrix} = \mathbf{AB}\begin{bmatrix} E_3 \\ I_3 \end{bmatrix}$$

and the matrix of the resultant four-terminal network is the product **AB**. This result can obviously be extended. If k four-terminal networks with matrices $\mathbf{A}^{(1)}, \mathbf{A}^{(2)}, \ldots, \mathbf{A}^{(k)}$ are connected in cascade as above, the resultant four-terminal network has matrix $\mathbf{A}^{(1)}\mathbf{A}^{(2)}\ldots\mathbf{A}^{(k)}$. In particular, if k identical four-terminal networks, each with matrix **A**, are connected in cascade they are equivalent to a single four-terminal network with matrix $\mathbf{A}^k$.

To illustrate this by a simple and trivial example we shall now derive the matrix of the star-connected impedance shown in Fig. 6 (*a*). This is obviously a cascade connection of a series impedance of the type shown in Fig. 6 (*b*) followed by a shunt impedance of the type shown in Fig. 6 (*c*) and finally another series impedance.

For the series impedance we obtain by inspection

$$E_1 = E_2 + ZI_2,$$

$$I_1 = I_2$$

so that

$$\begin{bmatrix} E_1 \\ I_1 \end{bmatrix} = \begin{bmatrix} 1 & Z \\ 0 & 1 \end{bmatrix}\begin{bmatrix} E_2 \\ I_2 \end{bmatrix}$$

and the associated matrix is $\begin{bmatrix} 1 & Z \\ 0 & 1 \end{bmatrix}$.

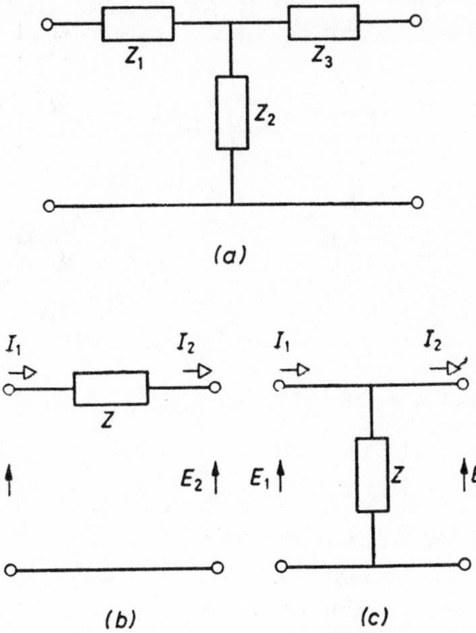

FIG. 6

Similarly for the shunt impedance we obtain

$$E_1 = E_2$$
$$I_1 = (1/Z)E_2 + I_2,$$

and the associated matrix is $\begin{bmatrix} 1 & 0 \\ 1/Z & 1 \end{bmatrix}$.

Combining the two previous results we can now very quickly obtain the matrix for the four-terminal network of Fig. 6 (*a*). It is a product of three matrices, viz.

$$\begin{bmatrix} 1 & Z_1 \\ 0 & 1 \end{bmatrix} \begin{bmatrix} 1 & 0 \\ 1/Z_2 & 1 \end{bmatrix} \begin{bmatrix} 1 & Z_3 \\ 0 & 1 \end{bmatrix} = \begin{bmatrix} 1 & Z_1 \\ 0 & 1 \end{bmatrix} \begin{bmatrix} 1 & Z_3 \\ 1/Z_2 & Z_3/Z_2+1 \end{bmatrix}$$
$$= \frac{1}{Z_2} \cdot \begin{bmatrix} Z_1+Z_2 & Z_2Z_3+Z_3Z_1+Z_1Z_2 \\ 1 & Z_2+Z_3 \end{bmatrix}.$$

This result can, of course, be obtained by inspection and the example has been chosen merely to illustrate the method. Another application of simple matrix multiplication is given by the network of Fig. 7.

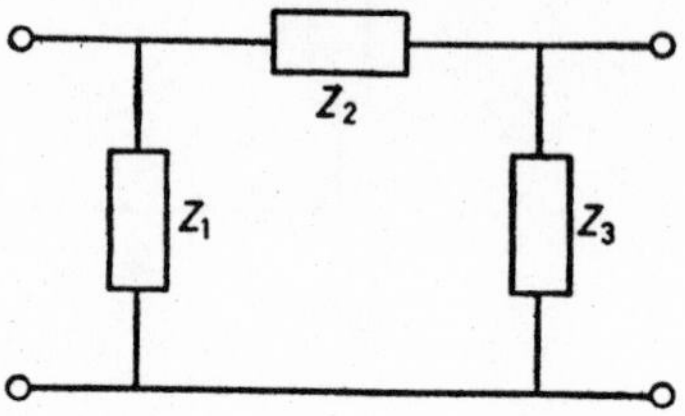

FIG. 7

The associated matrix for this network is

$$\begin{bmatrix} 1 & 0 \\ 1/Z_1 & 1 \end{bmatrix} \begin{bmatrix} 1 & Z_2 \\ 0 & 1 \end{bmatrix} \begin{bmatrix} 1 & 0 \\ 1/Z_3 & 1 \end{bmatrix} = \frac{1}{Z_1 Z_3} \begin{bmatrix} Z_1(Z_2+Z_3) & Z_1 Z_2 Z_3 \\ Z_1+Z_2+Z_3 & Z_3(Z_1+Z_2) \end{bmatrix}.$$

4·5 Reversed four-terminal networks

A four-terminal network need not, in general, be symmetric and different network equations are obtained for the *reversed* network, i.e. for the network having its input and output terminals interchanged. The relevant equations can be obtained by the following steps. From equation (21) we get

$$\begin{bmatrix} E_2 \\ I_2 \end{bmatrix} = \mathbf{A}^{-1} \begin{bmatrix} E_1 \\ I_1 \end{bmatrix} \quad \text{where} \quad \mathbf{A}^{-1} = \begin{bmatrix} d & -b \\ -c & a \end{bmatrix} \quad \text{since} \quad |\mathbf{A}| = 1.$$

However, if the output side (i.e. side 2) is made the input side (side 1), then the direction of current flow must be changed. Thus the signs of I_1 and I_2 must be reversed so that the last equation becomes

$$\begin{bmatrix} E_2 \\ I_2 \end{bmatrix} = \begin{bmatrix} d & b \\ c & a \end{bmatrix} \begin{bmatrix} E_1 \\ I_1 \end{bmatrix}.$$

Lastly, interchanging suffixes 1 and 2 (to conform with the convention adopted here that suffix 1 refers to the input and suffix 2 to the output) we obtain finally for the reversed four-terminal network

$$\begin{bmatrix} E_1 \\ I_1 \end{bmatrix} = \begin{bmatrix} d & b \\ c & a \end{bmatrix} \begin{bmatrix} E_2 \\ I_2 \end{bmatrix}$$

where $\begin{vmatrix} d & b \\ c & a \end{vmatrix} = 1.$

Hence the matrix of the reversed network is obtained from that of the original network by interchanging the principal diagonal elements a and d. Only when $a=d$ are the two networks the same and when this condition holds the network is said to be *reversible*. In this case the matrix has only three different elements a, b and c, and because the determinant of the matrix is equal to unity, viz. $a^2-bc=1$, only two parameters are needed for its complete specification. We then have $a=\sqrt{(1+bc)}$, and the matrix **A** is given by

$$\mathbf{A} = \begin{bmatrix} \sqrt{(1+bc)} & b \\ c & \sqrt{(1+bc)} \end{bmatrix}.$$

4·6 Characteristic impedance

Suppose that an impedance z' is connected at the exit of a four-terminal network with matrix $\begin{bmatrix} a & b \\ c & d \end{bmatrix}$. Then

$$E_2 = z'I_2.$$

The input impedance z is given by

$$z = \frac{E_1}{I_1} = \frac{aE_2+bI_2}{cE_2+dI_2} = \frac{az'+b}{cz'+d}.$$

If ζ, ζ' are the input, output impedances respectively for the reversed four-terminal network, we obtain similarly

$$\zeta = \frac{d\zeta'+b}{c\zeta'+a}.$$

We can now obtain the condition that $z=z'$. This is given by

$$z = \frac{az+b}{cz+d},$$

or

$$cz^2+(d-a)z-b = 0. \tag{22}$$

Similarly, the condition that $\zeta=\zeta'$ is

$$c\zeta^2+(a-d)\zeta-b = 0. \tag{23}$$

If z satisfies equation (22), then

$$c(-z)^2+(a-d)(-z)-b = 0,$$

so that $-z$ satisfies equation (23). Thus if z is a root of equation (22), $-z$ is a root of equation (23). It follows that, of the four roots of the two equations (22) and (23), two have non-negative and two have non-positive real parts. A physically admissible value of z or ζ must have non-negative real part and we are led to suppose that there is one value of z and one value of ζ with non-negative real part satisfying equations (22), (23) respectively. The proof of this is beyond the scope of this book, but it is immediately seen to be true for a reversible network (in which $a=d$) and also for a network in which b and c are real and positive. Calling these values z and ζ we have the following definition.

z is called the *characteristic impedance* of the network in the *direct sense* and ζ is that in the *reverse sense.* The roots of equation (22) are therefore z and $-\zeta$. If the network is reversible, $a=d$ and

$$z^2 = \zeta^2 = b/c,$$

so that $z=\zeta$.

4·7 Cascade connection of identical networks

Consider a cascade connection of n identical four-terminal networks, each of matrix $\mathbf{A}=\begin{bmatrix} a & b \\ c & d \end{bmatrix}$. The matrix of the resultant network is $\mathbf{A}^n$.

Now the eigenvalues of $\mathbf{A}$ are the roots of the equation

$$\begin{vmatrix} a-\lambda & b \\ c & d-\lambda \end{vmatrix} = 0,$$

i.e. $$\lambda^2-\lambda(a+d)+1 = 0, \quad \text{since} \quad ad-bc = 1.$$

Since the product of the roots of this equation is 1 we may denote the eigenvalues by e^{γ} and $e^{-\gamma}$. γ is, in general, complex, and since the sum of the roots of the characteristic equation is $(a+d)$ we have

$$e^{\gamma}+e^{-\gamma} = 2\cosh\gamma = a+d.$$

Let $\begin{bmatrix} q \\ 1 \end{bmatrix}$ be an eigenvector corresponding to the eigenvalue λ. Then

$$(a-\lambda)q+b = 0,$$

$$cq+d-\lambda = 0.$$

Eliminating λ we have

$$q(a-d-cq)+b = 0,$$

or $$cq^2+(d-a)q-b = 0,$$

which is identical with equation (22).

Thus $$q = z \quad \text{or} \quad -\zeta.$$

These roots are distinct unless

$$(d-a)^2+4bc = 0,$$

i.e. $$(d+a)^2 = 4 \quad (\text{since } bc = ad-1)$$

$$d+a = \pm 2.$$

Hence, if $d+a \neq \pm 2$, and

$$\mathbf{Q} = \begin{bmatrix} z & -\zeta \\ 1 & 1 \end{bmatrix}, \quad \mathbf{Q}^{-1} = \frac{1}{z+\zeta}\begin{bmatrix} 1 & \zeta \\ -1 & z \end{bmatrix},$$

$$\mathbf{A} = \mathbf{Q\Lambda Q}^{-1} \quad \text{where} \quad \mathbf{\Lambda} = \begin{bmatrix} e^{\gamma} & 0 \\ 0 & e^{-\gamma} \end{bmatrix}.$$

$$\begin{aligned}
\mathbf{A}^n &= (\mathbf{Q\Lambda Q}^{-1})(\mathbf{Q\Lambda Q}^{-1})\ldots(\mathbf{Q\Lambda Q}^{-1}) \quad (n \text{ factors}) \\
&= \mathbf{Q\Lambda}^n\mathbf{Q}^{-1} \\
&= \frac{1}{z+\zeta}\begin{bmatrix} z & -\zeta \\ 1 & 1 \end{bmatrix}\begin{bmatrix} e^{n\gamma} & 0 \\ 0 & e^{-n\gamma} \end{bmatrix}\begin{bmatrix} 1 & \zeta \\ -1 & z \end{bmatrix} \\
&= \frac{1}{z+\zeta}\begin{bmatrix} z & -\zeta \\ 1 & 1 \end{bmatrix}\begin{bmatrix} e^{n\gamma} & \zeta e^{n\gamma} \\ -e^{-n\gamma} & ze^{-n\gamma} \end{bmatrix} \\
&= \frac{1}{z+\zeta}\begin{bmatrix} ze^{n\gamma}+\zeta e^{-n\gamma} & z\zeta(e^{n\gamma}-e^{-n\gamma}) \\ e^{n\gamma}-e^{-n\gamma} & \zeta e^{n\gamma}+ze^{-n\gamma} \end{bmatrix}.
\end{aligned}$$

In the special case when the network **A** is reversible we have $z=\zeta$, so that

$$\begin{aligned}
\mathbf{A}^n &= \frac{1}{2z}\begin{bmatrix} z(e^{n\gamma}+e^{-n\gamma}) & z^2(e^{n\gamma}-e^{-n\gamma}) \\ e^{n\gamma}-e^{-n\gamma} & z(e^{n\gamma}+e^{-n\gamma}) \end{bmatrix} \\
&= \begin{bmatrix} \cosh n\gamma & z\sinh n\gamma \\ \frac{1}{z}\sinh n\gamma & \cosh n\gamma \end{bmatrix}.
\end{aligned}$$

We must now consider the special cases for which $a+d=\pm 2$ when the above method for determining $\mathbf{A}^n$ is no longer valid. If $a+d=2$, we can verify by induction that

$$\mathbf{A}^n = n\mathbf{A}-(n-1)\mathbf{1}. \tag{24}$$

For $$\mathbf{A}^2 = \begin{bmatrix} a & b \\ c & d \end{bmatrix}\begin{bmatrix} a & b \\ c & d \end{bmatrix} = \begin{bmatrix} a^2+bc & b(a+d) \\ c(a+d) & bc+d^2 \end{bmatrix}$$

$$= \begin{bmatrix} a(a+d)-1 & 2b \\ 2c & d(a+d)-1 \end{bmatrix} \quad (\text{since } bc = ad-1)$$

$$= \begin{bmatrix} 2a-1 & 2b \\ 2c & 2d-1 \end{bmatrix} = 2\begin{bmatrix} a & b \\ c & d \end{bmatrix} - \begin{bmatrix} 1 & 0 \\ 0 & 1 \end{bmatrix},$$

i.e. $\mathbf{A}^2 = 2\mathbf{A}-\mathbf{1}$.

Thus equation (24) holds when $n=2$.

Further, if

$$\mathbf{A}^k = k\mathbf{A}-(k-1)\mathbf{1},$$

then
$$\mathbf{A}^{k+1} = k\mathbf{A}^2-(k-1)\mathbf{A} = k(2\mathbf{A}-\mathbf{1})-(k-1)\mathbf{A}$$
$$= (k+1)\mathbf{A}-k\mathbf{1}.$$

Consequently, if equation (24) holds for $n=k$, it also holds for $n=k+1$. The equation is therefore valid for all positive integers $n \geqslant 2$, by induction, and it is clearly true when $n=1$. Similarly if $a+d=-2$, we have

$$\mathbf{A}^n = (-1)^{n+1}\{n\mathbf{A}+(n-1)\mathbf{1}\}. \tag{25}$$

For in this case

$$\mathbf{A}^2 = \begin{bmatrix} -2a-1 & -2b \\ -2c & -2d-1 \end{bmatrix} = -2\mathbf{A}-\mathbf{1},$$

and this is equation (25) for $n=2$.

Further, if $\mathbf{A}^k = (-1)^{k+1}\{k\mathbf{A}+(k-1)\mathbf{1}\},$

then
$$\mathbf{A}^{k+1} = (-1)^{k+1}\{k\mathbf{A}^2+(k-1)\mathbf{A}\}$$
$$= (-1)^{k+1}\{-2k\mathbf{A}-k\mathbf{1}+(k-1)\mathbf{A}\}$$
$$= (-1)^{k+2}\{(k+1)\mathbf{A}+k\mathbf{1}\}.$$

Equation (25) therefore holds for all positive integers $n \geqslant 2$ by induction, and is also true for $n=1$.

4·8 Wave propagation along a line of cascade connected networks

Consider an infinite number of identical four-terminal networks, each with matrix $\mathbf{A}=\begin{bmatrix} a & b \\ c & d \end{bmatrix}$, connected in cascade. Then if E_n, I_n are the input voltage and current for the nth element we have

$$\begin{bmatrix} E_n \\ I_n \end{bmatrix} = \mathbf{A}\begin{bmatrix} E_{n+1} \\ I_{n+1} \end{bmatrix}. \tag{26}$$

But for a single wave propagating along this line we have

$$\begin{bmatrix} E_{n+1} \\ I_{n+1} \end{bmatrix} = \mu\begin{bmatrix} E_n \\ I_n \end{bmatrix}, \tag{27}$$

where μ is a complex constant.

Thus, combining equations (26) and (27), we have

$$\begin{bmatrix} E_n \\ I_n \end{bmatrix} = \mu\mathbf{A}\begin{bmatrix} E_n \\ I_n \end{bmatrix},$$

or

$$\mathbf{A}\begin{bmatrix} E_n \\ I_n \end{bmatrix} = \frac{1}{\mu}\begin{bmatrix} E_n \\ I_n \end{bmatrix},$$

so that $1/\mu$ is an eigenvalue of $\mathbf{A}$.

There are thus two possible values of μ, viz. $1/\lambda_1$ and $1/\lambda_2$, where, as before,

$$\lambda_1 = e^{-\gamma}, \qquad \lambda_2 = e^{\gamma},$$

γ being a complex number. Let $\gamma = \alpha + j\beta$, where α and β are real.

Then $\mu = e^{\alpha}e^{j\beta}$ or $e^{-\alpha}e^{-j\beta}$ and these two values correspond to propagation in opposite directions along the line. α is the *attenuation constant*, and if $\alpha = 0$ there is no attenuation. Now

$$\cosh \gamma = \frac{e^{\gamma} + e^{-\gamma}}{2} = \frac{a+d}{2} \quad \text{(cf. §4·7).}$$

If $\alpha = 0$ this becomes

$$\cosh j\beta = \cos \beta = \frac{a+d}{2},$$

so that $a+d$ is real. Also

$$|a+d| = |2 \cos \beta| \leqslant 2.$$

We have therefore established the following two conditions for a pass band:

(i) $a+d$ is real;

(ii) $|a+d| \leqslant 2$.

Currents and voltages for which these conditions are satisfied are passed by the cascade arrangement, whilst those of other frequencies are attenuated.

4·9 Image impedances

Let z_1, z_2 be the impedances of a four-terminal network on open, closed circuit respectively. Then z_1 and z_2 are the two values of z given by the equation

$$z = \frac{az' + b}{cz' + d} = \frac{a + b/z'}{c + d/z'}$$

when z' is infinite and when z' is zero (cf. §4·6). Hence

$$z_1 = a/c, \qquad z_2 = b/d.$$

If ζ_1, ζ_2 are the corresponding impedances for the reversed four-terminal network,

$$\zeta_1 = d/c, \qquad \zeta_2 = b/a.$$

Then the geometric means of z_1, z_2 and of ζ_1, ζ_2, viz. $\sqrt{(ab/cd)}$ and $\sqrt{(bd/ac)}$, are called the *image impedances*. If the network is reversible, then $a=d$ and these two quantities are equal to one another and to the characteristic impedance of the circuit. For in this case

$$z = \zeta = \sqrt{(b/c)}.$$

It is interesting that one can obtain these impedances as characteristic impedances in the following manner. In the general case, consider the resultant four-terminal network formed by connecting in cascade a four-terminal network with matrix **A** followed by its reverse. The matrix of the resultant is

$$\begin{bmatrix} a & b \\ c & d \end{bmatrix} \begin{bmatrix} d & b \\ c & a \end{bmatrix} = \begin{bmatrix} ad+bc & 2ab \\ 2cd & ad+bc \end{bmatrix}$$

which represents a reversible four-terminal network. This has one characteristic impedance which is equal to $\sqrt{(ab/cd)}$, i.e. to the first image impedance of **A**. If the connection is made in the reverse order the matrix of the resultant is

$$\begin{bmatrix} d & b \\ c & a \end{bmatrix} \begin{bmatrix} a & b \\ c & d \end{bmatrix} = \begin{bmatrix} ad+bc & 2bd \\ 2ac & ad+bc \end{bmatrix}$$

which again represents a reversible four-terminal network. This has one characteristic impedance equal to $\sqrt{(bd/ac)}$, i.e. to the second image impedance of **A**.

4·10 The continuous transmission line

Consider a transmission line having a series impedance of Z per unit length and a shunt admittance of Y per unit length. We may regard the line as the limiting case as $\delta x \to 0$ of a cascade connection of identical symmetrical four-terminal networks, each corresponding to a length of line δx. Fig. 8 shows one such four-terminal network.

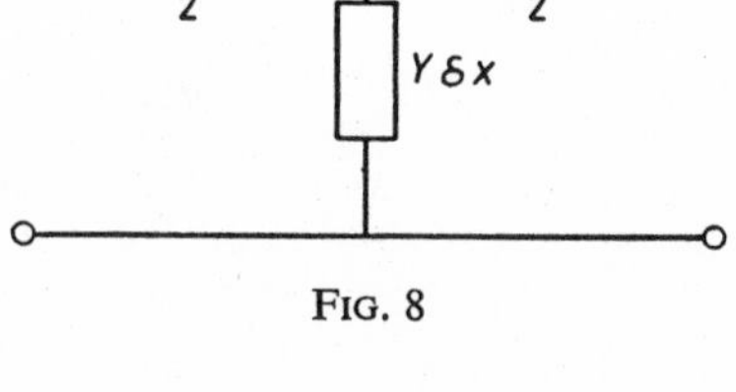

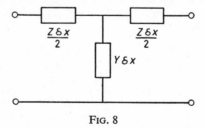

FIG. 8

This is a symmetrical T-network whose matrix **A** is given by

$$\mathbf{A} = \begin{bmatrix} 1 & Z\dfrac{\delta x}{2} \\ 0 & 1 \end{bmatrix} \begin{bmatrix} 1 & 0 \\ Y\,\delta x & 1 \end{bmatrix} \begin{bmatrix} 1 & Z\dfrac{\delta x}{2} \\ 0 & 1 \end{bmatrix}$$

$$= \begin{bmatrix} 1+ZY\dfrac{(\delta x)^2}{2} & Z\,\delta x+Z^2Y\dfrac{(\delta x)^3}{4} \\ Y\,\delta x & 1+ZY\dfrac{(\delta x)^2}{2} \end{bmatrix}.$$

Let the length of line be l and let $n\,\delta x = l$. Then

$$\mathbf{A} = \begin{bmatrix} 1+\dfrac{ZYl^2}{2n^2} & \dfrac{Zl}{n}+\dfrac{Z^2Yl^3}{4n^3} \\ \dfrac{Yl}{n} & 1+\dfrac{ZYl^2}{2n^2} \end{bmatrix}$$

and the matrix of the line is $\lim_{n\to\infty} \mathbf{A}^n$. As we should expect the matrix **A** corresponds to a reversible network, and with the usual notation

$$a = d = 1+\frac{ZYl^2}{2n^2}, \qquad c = \frac{Yl}{n}.$$

Now write $\theta^2 = l^2ZY$, $\theta = l\sqrt{(ZY)}$. It is immaterial which square root we take provided that we take the same one throughout. We then have

$$a = d = 1+\frac{\theta^2}{2n^2}.$$

But if e^{γ} and $e^{-\gamma}$ are the eigenvalues of **A** we have, as in §4·7,

$$e^{\gamma}+e^{-\gamma} = a+d = 2a.$$

Hence $$e^{2\gamma}-2a.e^{\gamma}+1 = 0$$

and we may take

$$e^{\gamma} = a+\sqrt{(a^2-1)} = 1+\frac{\theta^2}{2n^2}+\sqrt{\left(\frac{\theta^2}{n^2}+\frac{\theta^4}{4n^4}\right)}$$

$$= 1+\frac{\theta^2}{2n^2}+\frac{\theta}{n}\left\{1+\frac{\theta^2}{4n^2}\right\}^{1/2}$$

$$= 1+\frac{\theta^2}{2n^2}+\frac{\theta}{n}\left\{1+\frac{\theta^2}{8n^2}+\text{higher powers of }\frac{1}{n}\right\} \quad \text{if } n \text{ is large}$$

$$= 1+\frac{\theta}{n}+\frac{\theta^2}{2n^2}+\text{higher powers of }\frac{1}{n}.$$

Hence $$\gamma = \log_e\left\{1+\frac{\theta}{n}+\cdots\right\}$$

$$= \frac{\theta}{n}+\text{terms in } \frac{1}{n^2} \text{ and higher powers of } \frac{1}{n}.$$

It follows that

$$n\gamma \to \theta \quad \text{as} \quad n \to \infty.$$

If $\begin{bmatrix} z \\ 1 \end{bmatrix}$ is the eigenvector of $\mathbf{A}$ corresponding to the eigenvalue e^γ,

$$cz+d-e^\gamma = 0.$$

Hence $$z = \frac{e^\gamma-d}{c} = \frac{\theta/n+\text{higher powers of } 1/n}{Yl/n}$$

$$= \frac{\theta}{Yl}+\text{terms in } \frac{1}{n} \text{ and higher powers of } \frac{1}{n}.$$

It follows that $\lim\limits_{n\to\infty} z = \frac{\theta}{Yl} = z_0$, say.

Using the result obtained in §4·7 for the special case $a=d$ we have

$$\mathbf{A}^n = \begin{bmatrix} \cosh n\gamma & z \sinh n\gamma \\ (1/z) \sinh n\gamma & \cosh n\gamma \end{bmatrix}$$

and hence, letting $n \to \infty$,

$$\lim_{n\to\infty} \mathbf{A}^n = \begin{bmatrix} \cosh \theta & z_0 \sinh \theta \\ (1/z_0) \sinh \theta & \cosh \theta \end{bmatrix}.$$

This is the matrix of the continuous line.

Note that changing the sign of θ leaves $\cosh\theta$ unchanged. It reverses the sign of both z_0 and $\sinh\theta$ and therefore leaves both $z_0 \sinh\theta$ and $(1/z_0)\sinh\theta$ unchanged. Consequently it leaves the matrix $\lim\limits_{n\to\infty} \mathbf{A}^n$ unchanged and our earlier remark, that the sign chosen for θ is immaterial, is justified.

CHAPTER 5

Network Analysis on Loop and Node Basis

ANOTHER simple application of matrices is to establish the relevant equations for the solution of network problems. Any interconnection of passive and active circuit elements constitutes an electric network and the object of network analysis is to find the current responses which are produced in the network by the presence of the active elements. In the case of more complicated networks the general analysis is greatly facilitated by the use of a few elementary facts from the "theory of linear graphs" which forms a branch of topology. According to this only the geometrical pattern of a network is considered and no distinction is made between different types of physical elements of which it is composed. The basic elements, according to this theory, are branches, branch points or nodes and loops.

5·1 Trees, cotrees and loops

From the topological point of view a network consists of n *nodes* which are interconnected in some way in pairs by b *branches*. Starting at any node it is possible, usually in a number of different ways, to traverse adjacent branches and to return to the starting node. Such a closed path formed by network branches is known as a *loop*. We shall suppose the network to be connected, i.e. that it is possible to travel from any one node to any other along branches of the network. Very important in linear graph theory is the concept of a tree. This is a set of branches having the property that every node is connected to every other node (directly or indirectly) and such that removal of any single branch destroys this property. Now the nodes of a network may be interconnected in more than one way, so that every network has more than one tree. Fig. 9 (*a*) shows a simple network of 5 nodes and 7 branches and two possible trees are shown in Fig. 9 (*b*) and Fig. 9 (*c*). Now a complete tree may be formed by starting with any one branch and adjoining a second to it at one end to move on to a third node; from one of these three nodes we select a third branch along which we can move to a fourth node, and so on until all the nodes have been reached. Thus it will be clear that a complete tree contains $n-1$ branches which are known as the *branches-in-tree*. If from the set of all b branches of the network we remove the $n-1$ branches-in-tree, there remains a set of

$b-(n-1)=b-n+1$ branches known as the *cotree*. The branches of this set are known as *branches-out-of-tree* or *chords*. The cotrees

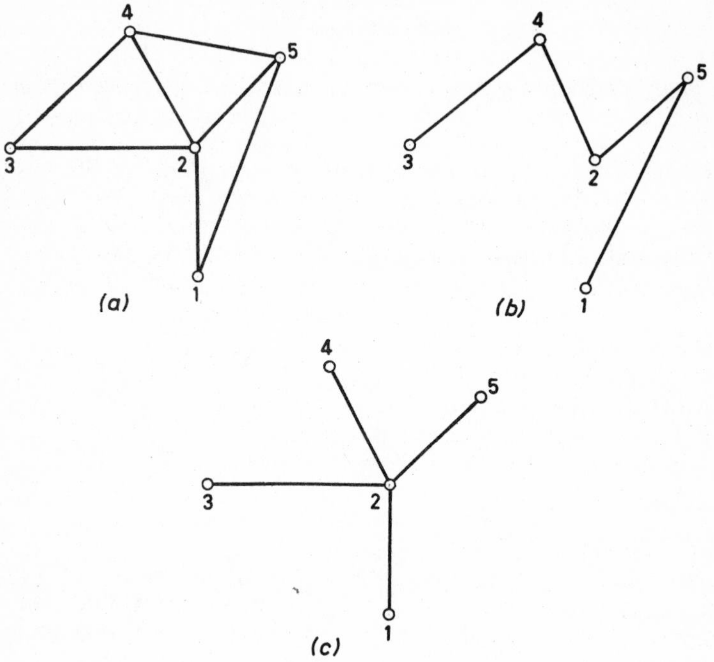

FIG. 9

corresponding to the two trees of Fig. 9 are shown in Fig. 10 (*a*) and (*b*).

It is the presence of these out-of-tree branches which gives rise to loops in the network or, in the case of an electrical network, which

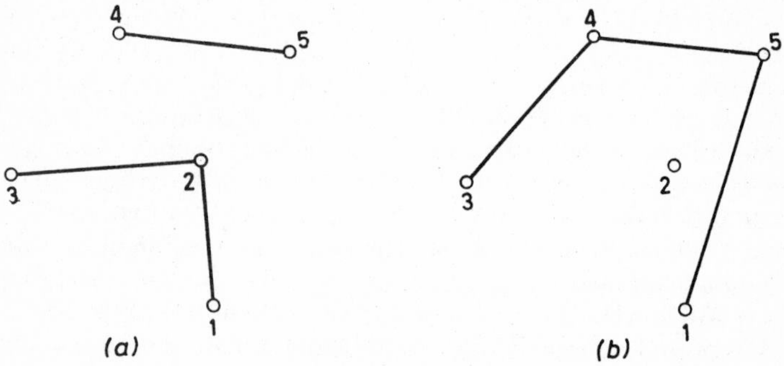

FIG. 10

makes it possible for currents to flow. Each branch of such a cotree determines uniquely a loop consisting of that branch together with those branches of the corresponding complete tree that connect the nodes at its end. For an electric network, if the loop currents of such a set of independent loops are known, all b branch currents are then uniquely determined. Let l be the number of independent loops. Then clearly $l=b-n+1$, since l is equal to the number of branches in the cotree. Since the out-of-tree branches determine uniquely a set of independent loops, they are sometimes referred to as *independent branches.*

5·2 Analysis of networks on the loop basis

The object is to set up a system of equations from which the independent loop currents can be determined for, as mentioned already, once this set of currents is known, the currents in all the branches can be calculated. To do this we assign quite arbitrarily to each of the b branches a positive direction for current flow. The direction assigned to each branch of the cotree determines a positive sense of current circulation for the corresponding loop. If the circuit can be mapped on a plane these directions are always chosen so that the positive sense for all loop currents is clockwise. In this case the loops are usually referred to as *meshes.* We now number the loops from 1 to l and the branches from 1 to b, and we define a matrix $\mathbf{C} = [c_{hk}]$ of order $l \times b$ as follows:

$$c_{hk} = 0 \quad \text{if branch } k \text{ is not part of loop } h;$$

otherwise

$$c_{hk} = \begin{cases} +1 & \text{if the positive sense of current flow in branch } k \\ & \text{coincides with that of loop } h, \\ -1 & \text{if the positive sense of current flow in branch } k \\ & \text{is opposite to that of loop } h. \end{cases}$$

The matrix **C** is known as the *connection matrix on a loop basis* and it specifies completely and uniquely the way in which the various branches are interconnected to form a set of independent loops. Row h of **C** contains non-zero entries only in those places whose column numbers correspond to branches forming part of loop h. A glance at row h, therefore, tells us at once exactly which branches form loop h. Again, each column contains either one or two non-zero entries. If column k has one non-zero entry, in row p, then branch k forms part of loop p and is in no other loop. On the other hand, if column k has non-zero entries in rows p and q, then branch k is common to loops p and q.

Now Kirchhoff's voltage law states that if v_k is the potential drop in the kth branch, then

$$\sum v_k = 0,$$

the sum being taken over all the branches in a given loop. There are consequently l such equations, one for each loop. It is easily seen that the equation for loop h is

$$\sum_{k=1}^{b} c_{hk}v_k = 0$$

so that the set of l equations can be written in matrix form

$$\mathbf{C}\{v_k\} = \mathbf{0}, \tag{28}$$

where $\{v_k\} = \{v_1, v_2, \ldots, v_b\}$.

Now if e_k is the e.m.f., i_k the current and z_k the impedance of the kth branch,

$$v_k = z_k i_k - e_k \quad (k = 1, 2, \ldots, b),$$

or

$$\begin{bmatrix} v_1 \\ v_2 \\ \cdot \\ v_b \end{bmatrix} = \begin{bmatrix} z_1 & 0 & \ldots & 0 \\ 0 & z_2 & \ldots & 0 \\ \cdot & \cdot & \cdot\ \cdot\ \cdot & \cdot \\ 0 & 0 & \ldots & z_b \end{bmatrix} \begin{bmatrix} i_1 \\ i_2 \\ \cdot \\ i_b \end{bmatrix} - \begin{bmatrix} e_1 \\ e_2 \\ \cdot \\ e_b \end{bmatrix}.$$

The matrix $[z_{hk}]$ is diagonal.

If, however, the circuit contains inductances, so that there is coupling between branches, this matrix is no longer diagonal. If z_{kk} is the self-impedance of branch k, and $z_{kh} = z_{hk}$ is the mutual impedance of branches h and k,

$$v_k = \sum_{h=1}^{b} z_{kh} i_h - e_k \quad (k = 1, 2, \ldots, b),$$

or

$$\begin{bmatrix} v_1 \\ v_2 \\ \cdot \\ v_b \end{bmatrix} = \begin{bmatrix} z_{11} & z_{12} & \ldots & z_{1b} \\ z_{21} & z_{22} & \ldots & z_{2b} \\ \cdot & \cdot & \cdot\ \cdot\ \cdot & \cdot \\ z_{b1} & z_{b2} & \ldots & z_{bb} \end{bmatrix} \begin{bmatrix} i_1 \\ i_2 \\ \cdot \\ i_b \end{bmatrix} - \begin{bmatrix} e_1 \\ e_2 \\ \cdot \\ e_b \end{bmatrix}.$$

This may be written

$$\{v_k\} = [z_{hk}]\{i_k\} - \{e_k\},$$

where the matrix of impedances $[z_{hk}]$ is symmetric.

Hence, using equation (28),

$$\mathbf{C}\{v_k\} = \mathbf{0} = \mathbf{C}[z_{hk}]\{i_k\} - \mathbf{C}\{e_k\}. \tag{29}$$

Let $I_1, I_2, \ldots, I_l$ be the loop currents. Then the current flowing through a branch common to two loops is (with the sign convention already mentioned) either the sum or the difference of the two loop currents. The current flowing through a branch which forms part of only one loop is either plus or minus the loop current. Clearly

$$\begin{aligned} i_k &= c_{1k}I_1 + c_{2k}I_2 + \cdots + c_{lk}I_l \\ &= c^t_{k1}I_1 + c^t_{k2}I_2 + \cdots + c^t_{kl}I_l \quad (k = 1, 2, \ldots, b). \end{aligned}$$

This set of b equations can be written in matrix form

$$\{i_k\} = \mathbf{C}^t\mathbf{I} \tag{30}$$

where $\mathbf{I} = \{I_1, I_2, \ldots, I_l\}$, and $\mathbf{C}^t$ is the transpose of $\mathbf{C}$. Let $E_1, E_2, \ldots, E_l$ be the loop e.m.f.'s. Then E_h is the algebraic sum of the branch e.m.f.'s for those branches forming loop h. Thus

$$E_h = \sum_{k=1}^{b} c_{hk}e_k \quad (h = 1, 2, \ldots, l)$$

or $$\mathbf{E} = \mathbf{C}\{e_k\}, \tag{31}$$

where $$\mathbf{E} = \{E_1, E_2, \ldots, E_l\}.$$

Substituting in equation (29) for $\{i_k\}$ from equation (30) and for $\mathbf{C}\{e_k\}$ from equation (31) we obtain

$$\mathbf{E} = \mathbf{C}[z_{hk}]\mathbf{C}^t\mathbf{I}.$$

$\mathbf{C}[z_{hk}]\mathbf{C}^t$ is a square matrix of order $l \times l$, and denoting this by $\mathbf{Z}$ we have

$$\mathbf{E} = \mathbf{ZI}.$$

$\mathbf{Z}$ is clearly a symmetric matrix, since $z_{hk} = z_{kh}$, and it is known as the *loop impedance matrix.*

In the above analysis any branch may be a series connection of resistances, inductances and capacitances. The impedance matrix $\mathbf{Z}$ will, however, assume a much simpler form if we consider each passive element as a separate branch. Thus a branch consisting of a series connection of R, L and C is replaced by three branches, one a pure resistance R, one a pure inductance L and one a pure capacitance C. Let us suppose that the new set of b branches consists of λ inductances, ρ resistances and σ capacitances. The numbering of the branches was completely arbitrary and we may, without loss of generality, number first all the inductance branches consecutively from 1 to λ, then all the resistance branches from $\lambda+1$ to $\lambda+\rho$ and finally all the capacitance branches from $\lambda+\rho+1$ to $\lambda+\rho+\sigma=b$. Now in equation (29) z_{hk} $(h\neq k)$ is the mutual impedance of branches h and k and this is clearly zero unless these branches contain inductances. Thus in this case

$$z_{hk} = 0 \ (h \neq k) \quad \text{unless} \quad 1 \leqslant h \leqslant \lambda \quad \text{and} \quad 1 \leqslant k \leqslant \lambda.$$

Moreover in this range $z_{hk}=pl_{hk}$, where p has the usual meaning (and is equal to $j\omega$ for steady state quantities), l_{hk} $(h\neq k)$ is the mutual inductance of branches h and k, and l_{hh} is the self inductance of branch h. We therefore have for the inductance branches

$$\begin{bmatrix} v_1 \\ v_2 \\ \cdot \\ v_\lambda \end{bmatrix} = p \begin{bmatrix} l_{11} & l_{12} & \dots & l_{1\lambda} \\ l_{21} & l_{22} & \dots & l_{2\lambda} \\ \cdot & \cdot & \cdot & \cdot \\ l_{\lambda 1} & l_{\lambda 2} & \dots & l_{\lambda\lambda} \end{bmatrix} \begin{bmatrix} i_1 \\ i_2 \\ \cdot \\ i_\lambda \end{bmatrix} - \begin{bmatrix} e_1 \\ e_2 \\ \cdot \\ e_\lambda \end{bmatrix}. \tag{32}$$

The $\lambda\times\lambda$ symmetric matrix $[l_{hk}]$ is called the *branch inductance matrix*.

Similarly for the resistance branches, for which

$$z_{hk} = 0 \quad (h \neq k, \quad \lambda < h \leqslant \lambda+\rho, \quad \lambda < k \leqslant \lambda+\rho)$$

and $z_{hh}=r_h$, the resistance of branch h $(\lambda<h\leqslant\lambda+\rho)$,

$$\begin{bmatrix} v_{\lambda+1} \\ v_{\lambda+2} \\ \cdot \\ v_{\lambda+\rho} \end{bmatrix} = \begin{bmatrix} r_{\lambda+1} & 0 & \dots & 0 \\ 0 & r_{\lambda+2} & \dots & 0 \\ \cdot & \cdot & \cdot & \cdot \\ 0 & 0 & \dots & r_{\lambda+\rho} \end{bmatrix} \begin{bmatrix} i_{\lambda+1} \\ i_{\lambda+2} \\ \cdot \\ i_{\lambda+\rho} \end{bmatrix} - \begin{bmatrix} e_{\lambda+1} \\ e_{\lambda+2} \\ \cdot \\ e_{\lambda+\rho} \end{bmatrix}. \tag{33}$$

For the capacitance branches

$$z_{hk} = 0 \quad (h \neq k, \quad \lambda+\rho < h \leqslant b, \quad \lambda+\rho < k \leqslant b)$$

and $$z_{hh} = (1/p)s_{hh} \quad (\lambda+\rho < h \leqslant b),$$

where s_{hh} is the elastance of branch h. Then

$$\begin{bmatrix} v_{\lambda+\rho+1} \\ v_{\lambda+\rho+2} \\ \cdot \\ v_b \end{bmatrix} = \frac{1}{p} \begin{bmatrix} s_{\lambda+\rho+1} & 0 & \dots & 0 \\ 0 & s_{\lambda+\rho+2} & \dots & 0 \\ \cdot & \cdot & \cdot & \cdot \\ 0 & 0 & \dots & s_b \end{bmatrix} \begin{bmatrix} i_{\lambda+\rho+1} \\ i_{\lambda+\rho+2} \\ \cdot \\ i_b \end{bmatrix} - \begin{bmatrix} e_{\lambda+\rho+1} \\ e_{\lambda+\rho+2} \\ \cdot \\ e_b \end{bmatrix}. \tag{34}$$

If we write

$$\{v^{(\lambda)}\} = \{v_1, v_2, \dots, v_\lambda\},$$
$$\{v^{(\rho)}\} = \{v_{\lambda+1}, v_{\lambda+2}, \dots, v_{\lambda+\rho}\},$$
$$\{v^{(\sigma)}\} = \{v_{\lambda+\rho+1}, v_{\lambda+\rho+2}, \dots, v_b\}$$

and similarly for the vectors $\{i\}$ and $\{e\}$, the three equations (32), (33) and (34) can be combined and written in partitioned form

$$\begin{bmatrix} v^{(\lambda)} \\ v^{(\rho)} \\ v^{(\sigma)} \end{bmatrix} = \begin{bmatrix} p[l_{hk}] & \mathbf{0} & \mathbf{0} \\ \mathbf{0} & [r] & \mathbf{0} \\ \mathbf{0} & \mathbf{0} & \frac{1}{p}[s] \end{bmatrix} \begin{bmatrix} i^{(\lambda)} \\ i^{(\rho)} \\ i^{(\sigma)} \end{bmatrix} - \begin{bmatrix} e^{(\lambda)} \\ e^{(\rho)} \\ e^{(\sigma)} \end{bmatrix}. \tag{35}$$

$p[l_{hk}]$, $[r]$, $\frac{1}{p}[s]$ are of orders $\lambda\times\lambda$, $\rho\times\rho$, $\sigma\times\sigma$ respectively, the first being symmetric and the other two diagonal matrices. The zeros are all zero matrices of appropriate order. If the matrix $\mathbf{C}$ is constructed as before, we have

$$\mathbf{E} = \mathbf{C}\begin{bmatrix} p[l_{hk}] & \mathbf{0} & \mathbf{0} \\ \mathbf{0} & [r] & \mathbf{0} \\ \mathbf{0} & \mathbf{0} & \frac{1}{p}[s] \end{bmatrix}\mathbf{C}^t\mathbf{I} = \mathbf{ZI}. \tag{36}$$

If $\mathbf{C}_{(\lambda)}$, $\mathbf{C}_{(\rho)}$, $\mathbf{C}_{(\sigma)}$ are the matrices formed by the first λ, the next ρ and the final σ columns of the $l\times b$ matrix $\mathbf{C}$, we can partition $\mathbf{C}$ and write

$$\begin{aligned} \mathbf{Z} &= [\mathbf{C}_{(\lambda)} \quad \mathbf{C}_{(\rho)} \quad \mathbf{C}_{(\sigma)}]\begin{bmatrix} p[l_{hk}] & \mathbf{0} & \mathbf{0} \\ \mathbf{0} & [r] & \mathbf{0} \\ \mathbf{0} & \mathbf{0} & \frac{1}{p}[s] \end{bmatrix}\begin{bmatrix} \mathbf{C}^t_{(\lambda)} \\ \mathbf{C}^t_{(\rho)} \\ \mathbf{C}^t_{(\sigma)} \end{bmatrix} \\ &= p\mathbf{C}_{(\lambda)}[l_{hk}]\mathbf{C}^t_{(\lambda)} + \mathbf{C}_{(\rho)}[r]\mathbf{C}^t_{(\rho)} + \frac{1}{p}\mathbf{C}_{(\sigma)}[s]\mathbf{C}^t_{(\sigma)} \\ &= p\mathbf{L} + \mathbf{R} + \frac{1}{p}\mathbf{S}. \end{aligned}$$

L, **R**, **S** are called the *loop inductance*, *resistance*, *elastance matrices* respectively.

Now for meshes the matrices **R** and **S** can be written down by inspection. For in this case, assuming the same positive sense for all mesh currents, we have

$$R_{hk} = \sum_q c_{h,\lambda+q} r_q c_{k,\lambda+q}.$$

Now $c_{h,\lambda+q}c_{k,\lambda+q}$ is zero unless branch $\lambda+q$ (i.e. the qth resistance branch) belongs to both meshes h and k. In this case, if $h \neq k$,

$$c_{h,\lambda+q}c_{k,\lambda+q} = -1$$

and

$$R_{hk} = -\sum_q r_q = R_{kh},$$

so that R_{hk} is the negative of the sum of the resistances common to meshes h and k. Also

$$R_{hh} = \sum_q (c_{h,\lambda+q})^2 r_q = \sum r_q,$$

so that R_{hh} is the sum of the resistances in mesh h. Thus we can at once write down the symmetric resistance matrix **R**, and similarly we can write down the symmetric elastance matrix **S**. Consequently we need apply the above method only in the determination of the more complicated inductance matrix.

We shall now illustrate the two methods described by solving an example in both ways.

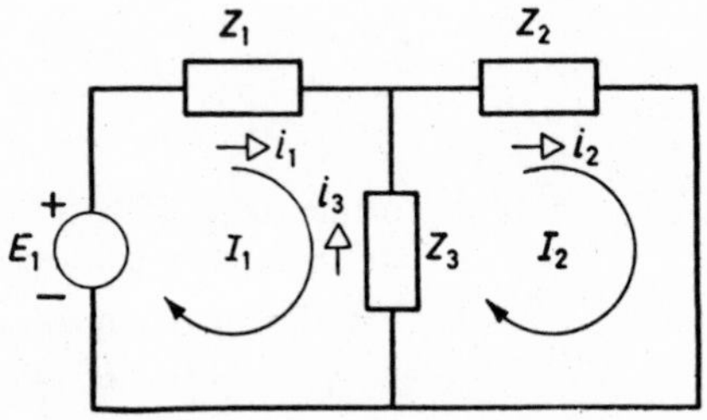

FIG. 11

Fig. 11 illustrates a three-branch, two-mesh network. With the usual notation the branch impedance matrix may be written

$$\begin{bmatrix} pl_{11}+r_1+\frac{1}{p}\,s_1 & pl_{12} & pl_{13} \\ pl_{21} & pl_{22}+r_2+\frac{1}{p}\,s_2 & pl_{23} \\ pl_{31} & pl_{32} & pl_{33}+r_3+\frac{1}{p}\,s_3 \end{bmatrix}.$$

In this case, the meshes and branches being numbered as in the figure,

$$\mathbf{C} = \begin{bmatrix} 1 & 0 & -1 \\ 0 & 1 & 1 \end{bmatrix}.$$

The mesh impedance matrix **Z** can therefore be written down as follows:

$$\mathbf{Z} = \begin{bmatrix} 1 & 0 & -1 \\ 0 & 1 & 1 \end{bmatrix} \begin{bmatrix} pl_{11}+r_1+(1/p)s_1 & pl_{12} & pl_{13} \\ pl_{21} & pl_{22}+r_2+(1/p)s_2 & pl_{23} \\ pl_{31} & pl_{32} & pl_{33}+r_3+(1/p)s_3 \end{bmatrix} \begin{bmatrix} 1 & 0 \\ 0 & 1 \\ -1 & 1 \end{bmatrix}$$

$$= \begin{bmatrix} 1 & 0 & -1 \\ 0 & 1 & 1 \end{bmatrix} \begin{bmatrix} pl_{11}+r_1+\frac{1}{p}s_1-pl_{13} & pl_{12}+pl_{13} \\ pl_{12}-pl_{23} & pl_{22}+r_2+\frac{1}{p}s_2+pl_{23} \\ pl_{13}-pl_{33}-r_3-\frac{1}{p}s_3 & pl_{23}+pl_{33}+r_3+\frac{1}{p}s_3 \end{bmatrix}$$

$$= \begin{bmatrix} p(l_{11}-2l_{13}+l_{33})+(r_1+r_3)+\frac{1}{p}(s_1+s_3) & p(l_{12}+l_{13}-l_{23}-l_{33})-r_3-\frac{1}{p}s_3 \\ p(l_{12}-l_{23}+l_{13}-l_{33})-r_3-\frac{1}{p}s_3 & p(l_{22}+2l_{23}+l_{33})+(r_2+r_3)+\frac{1}{p}(s_2+s_3) \end{bmatrix}$$

$$= p\begin{bmatrix} l_{11}-2l_{13}+l_{33} & l_{12}+l_{13}-l_{23}-l_{33} \\ l_{12}+l_{13}-l_{23}-l_{33} & l_{22}+2l_{23}+l_{33} \end{bmatrix} + \begin{bmatrix} r_1+r_3 & -r_3 \\ -r_3 & r_2+r_3 \end{bmatrix} + \frac{1}{p}\begin{bmatrix} s_1+s_3 & -s_3 \\ -s_3 & s_2+s_3 \end{bmatrix}$$

$$= p\mathbf{L}+\mathbf{R}+\frac{1}{p}\mathbf{S}.$$

We then have

$$\begin{bmatrix} E_1 \\ 0 \end{bmatrix} = \mathbf{Z}\begin{bmatrix} I_1 \\ I_2 \end{bmatrix}.$$

Alternatively we may consider the network as having two meshes and nine branches (three inductances, three resistances and three elastances). The mesh (or loop) resistance matrix is given by:

R_{11} = sum of resistances in mesh 1 = r_1+r_3,

R_{22} = sum of resistances in mesh 2 = r_2+r_3,

$R_{12} = R_{21}$ = −(sum of resistances common to meshes 1 and 2)

$= -r_3$.

Thus
$$\mathbf{R} = \begin{bmatrix} r_1+r_3 & -r_3 \\ -r_3 & r_2+r_3 \end{bmatrix},$$

and similarly
$$\mathbf{S} = \begin{bmatrix} s_1+s_3 & -s_3 \\ -s_3 & s_2+s_3 \end{bmatrix}.$$

In this case $\mathbf{C} = \begin{bmatrix} 1 & 0 & -1 \\ 0 & 1 & 1 \end{bmatrix}$, i.e. the **C** above, and

$$\mathbf{L} = \begin{bmatrix} 1 & 0 & -1 \\ 0 & 1 & 1 \end{bmatrix} \begin{bmatrix} l_{11} & l_{12} & l_{13} \\ l_{12} & l_{22} & l_{23} \\ l_{13} & l_{23} & l_{33} \end{bmatrix} \begin{bmatrix} 1 & 0 \\ 0 & 1 \\ -1 & 1 \end{bmatrix}.$$

Since only the inductance branches give rise to any difficulty we now consider a more complicated circuit containing only inductances. This network is not connected in the topological sense, but because of the inductive coupling it can be treated as a connected network.

Fig. 12 shows five inductances which are inter-connected to form three meshes. For the indicated directions of the branch currents the

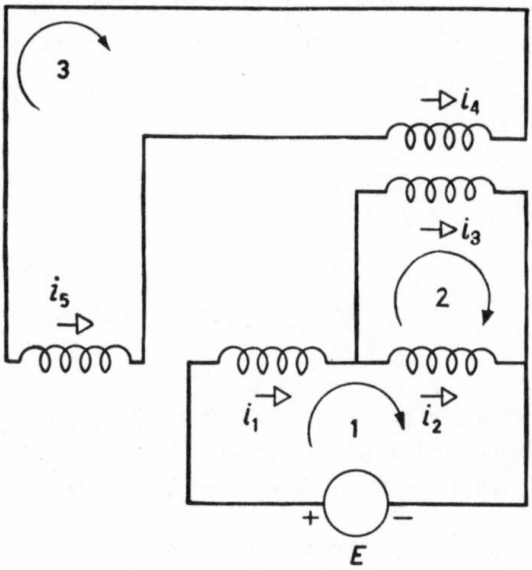

FIG. 12

numerical values of the coefficients of the self and mutual inductances are: $l_{11}=2$, $l_{22}=2$, $l_{33}=4$, $l_{44}=2$, $l_{55}=4$, $l_{12}=2$, $l_{15}=-4$ and $l_{34}=2$. All the remaining coefficients are zero. Establish the mesh equations.

For this network the connection matrix **C** is given by

$$\mathbf{C} = \begin{bmatrix} 1 & 1 & 0 & 0 & 0 \\ 0 & -1 & 1 & 0 & 0 \\ 0 & 0 & 0 & -1 & -1 \end{bmatrix},$$

and hence the inductance matrix **L** is given by

$$\mathbf{L} = \begin{bmatrix} 1 & 1 & 0 & 0 & 0 \\ 0 & -1 & 1 & 0 & 0 \\ 0 & 0 & 0 & -1 & -1 \end{bmatrix} \begin{bmatrix} 2 & 2 & 0 & 0 & -4 \\ 2 & 2 & 0 & 0 & 0 \\ 0 & 0 & 4 & 2 & 0 \\ 0 & 0 & 2 & 2 & 0 \\ -4 & 0 & 0 & 0 & 4 \end{bmatrix} \begin{bmatrix} 1 & 0 & 0 \\ 1 & -1 & 0 \\ 0 & 1 & 0 \\ 0 & 0 & -1 \\ 0 & 0 & -1 \end{bmatrix}$$

$$= \begin{bmatrix} 1 & 1 & 0 & 0 & 0 \\ 0 & -1 & 1 & 0 & 0 \\ 0 & 0 & 0 & -1 & -1 \end{bmatrix} \begin{bmatrix} 4 & -2 & 4 \\ 4 & -2 & 0 \\ 0 & 4 & -2 \\ 0 & 2 & -2 \\ -4 & 0 & -4 \end{bmatrix}$$

$$= \begin{bmatrix} 8 & -4 & 4 \\ -4 & 6 & -2 \\ 4 & -2 & 6 \end{bmatrix}.$$

The mesh equations are therefore

$$\begin{bmatrix} E \\ 0 \\ 0 \end{bmatrix} = p \begin{bmatrix} 8 & -4 & 4 \\ -4 & 6 & -2 \\ 4 & -2 & 6 \end{bmatrix} \begin{bmatrix} I_1 \\ I_2 \\ I_3 \end{bmatrix}.$$

5·3 Analysis of networks on the node basis

In the preceding analysis use was made of Kirchhoff's voltage law, which was applied to a set of independent network loops. It was shown how such a set of loops could always be found, using the concepts of tree and cotree, and how the relevant network equations could be obtained with the aid of the loop connection matrix.

An alternative procedure which makes use of the Kirchhoff current law is referred to as the *network analysis on the node basis*. We now assume that the network contains only current sources. If there are voltage sources present we may replace them by equivalent current sources (Norton's theorem). Kirchhoff's current law states that the sum of the currents arriving at any node is equal to the sum of those leaving it. Let us consider a network having $n+1$ nodes and b branches. We select one node as a reference node and assume its potential to be zero, and number the remaining nodes from 1 to n. We define an $n \times b$ matrix $\mathbf{B}=[b_{hk}]$ as follows:

$$b_{hk} = 0 \quad \text{if branch } k \text{ does not terminate at node } h.$$

$$\text{Otherwise } b_{hk} = \begin{cases} +1 & \text{if current } i_k \text{ leaves node } h, \\ -1 & \text{if current } i_k \text{ enters node } h. \end{cases}$$

The matrix **B** is known as the *node connection matrix*. From the definition one can see that the number of its rows is equal to the number of nodes n, and the number of its columns is equal to the number of branches b.

Let I_h be the sum of the source currents entering node h.

Then, using Kirchhoff's law,

$$I_h = \sum_{k=1}^{b} b_{hk} i_k$$

or

$$\mathbf{I} = \mathbf{B}\{i_k\}. \tag{37}$$

But when $\{e_k\}=\mathbf{0}$, equation (35) becomes

$$\{v_k\} = \begin{bmatrix} p[l_{hk}] & \mathbf{0} & \mathbf{0} \\ \mathbf{0} & [r] & \mathbf{0} \\ \mathbf{0} & \mathbf{0} & \frac{1}{p}[s] \end{bmatrix} \{i_k\}$$

so that

$$\{i_k\} = \begin{bmatrix} \frac{1}{p}[l_{hk}^{-1}] & \mathbf{0} & \mathbf{0} \\ \mathbf{0} & [r^{-1}] & \mathbf{0} \\ \mathbf{0} & \mathbf{0} & p[s^{-1}] \end{bmatrix} \{v_k\} \tag{38}$$

where $[l_{hk}^{-1}]$, $[r^{-1}]$, $[s^{-1}]$ are the reciprocals of $[l_{hk}]$, $[r]$, $[s]$ respectively.

Let $V_1, V_2, \ldots, V_n$ be the node voltages. Then, since v_k is the difference of the voltages of the nodes at the extremities of branch k, we may write

$$\begin{aligned} v_k &= b_{1k}V_1 + b_{2k}V_2 + \cdots + b_{nk}V_n \\ &= b_{k1}^t V_1 + b_{k2}^t V_2 + \cdots + b_{kn}^t V_n, \end{aligned}$$

i.e.

$$\{v_k\} = \mathbf{B}^t\mathbf{V}. \tag{39}$$

Combining equations (37), (38) and (39) we have

$$\mathbf{I} = \mathbf{B}\begin{bmatrix} \frac{1}{p}[l_{hk}^{-1}] & 0 & 0 \\ 0 & [r^{-1}] & 0 \\ 0 & 0 & p[s^{-1}] \end{bmatrix}\mathbf{B}^t\mathbf{V} = \mathbf{YV}, \quad \text{say.}$$

Y is called the admittance matrix and, as with **Z**, using a similar notation, we may write

$$\mathbf{Y} = \frac{1}{p}\,\mathbf{\Gamma}+\mathbf{G}+p\mathbf{C},$$

where

$$\mathbf{\Gamma} = \mathbf{B}_{(\lambda)}[l_{hk}^{-1}]\mathbf{B}_{(\lambda)}^t, \qquad \mathbf{G} = \mathbf{B}_{(\rho)}[r^{-1}]\mathbf{B}_{(\rho)}^t, \qquad \mathbf{C} = \mathbf{B}_{(\sigma)}[s^{-1}]\mathbf{B}_{(\sigma)}^t.$$

G and **C** may be written down by inspection, as before.

g_{hh} = sum of conductances of branches terminating at node h.

If $h \neq k$,

g_{hk} = −(sum of conductances of branches terminating at nodes h and k).

Similar formulae hold for the elements of the matrix **C**.

EXAMPLE.

Consider the circuit of Fig. 13 where the parameters have the following values:

$$l_{11} = 1, \quad l_{22} = 2, \quad l_{33} = 2, \quad l_{12} = -1, \quad l_{13} = -2,$$
$$l_{23} = 1, \quad r_4 = 1/2, \quad s_5 = 1, \quad s_6 = 1/3.$$

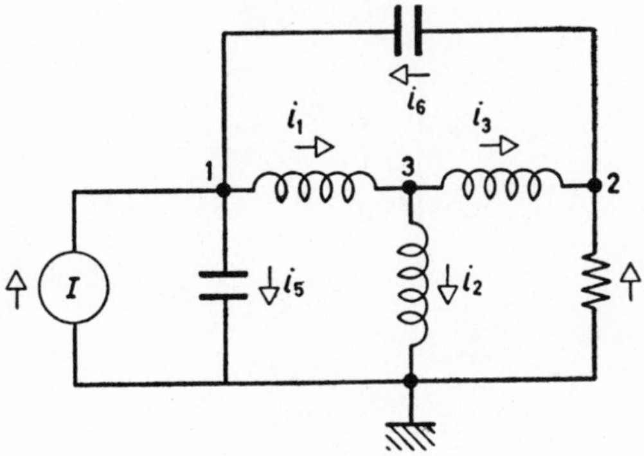

FIG. 13

By inspection we see that

$$\mathbf{G} = \begin{bmatrix} 0 & 0 & 0 \\ 0 & 2 & 0 \\ 0 & 0 & 0 \end{bmatrix}, \quad \mathbf{C} = \begin{bmatrix} 1+3 & -3 & 0 \\ -3 & 3 & 0 \\ 0 & 0 & 0 \end{bmatrix},$$

$$\mathbf{B}_{(\lambda)} = \begin{bmatrix} 1 & 0 & 0 \\ 0 & 0 & -1 \\ -1 & 1 & 1 \end{bmatrix},$$

$$[l_{hk}] = \begin{bmatrix} 1 & -1 & -2 \\ -1 & 2 & 1 \\ -2 & 1 & 2 \end{bmatrix}, \qquad [l_{hk}^{-1}] = -\frac{1}{3}\begin{bmatrix} 3 & 0 & 3 \\ 0 & -2 & 1 \\ 3 & 1 & 1 \end{bmatrix},$$

$$\mathbf{\Gamma} = -\frac{1}{3}\begin{bmatrix} 1 & 0 & 0 \\ 0 & 0 & -1 \\ -1 & 1 & 1 \end{bmatrix}\begin{bmatrix} 3 & 0 & 3 \\ 0 & -2 & 1 \\ 3 & 1 & 1 \end{bmatrix}\begin{bmatrix} 1 & 0 & -1 \\ 0 & 0 & 1 \\ 0 & -1 & 1 \end{bmatrix}$$

$$= -\frac{1}{3}\begin{bmatrix} 1 & 0 & 0 \\ 0 & 0 & -1 \\ -1 & 1 & 1 \end{bmatrix}\begin{bmatrix} 3 & -3 & 0 \\ 0 & -1 & -1 \\ 3 & -1 & -1 \end{bmatrix}$$

$$= -\frac{1}{3}\begin{bmatrix} 3 & -3 & 0 \\ -3 & 1 & 1 \\ 0 & 1 & -2 \end{bmatrix},$$

$$\mathbf{Y} = \frac{1}{p}\mathbf{\Gamma} + \mathbf{G} + p\mathbf{C} = \begin{bmatrix} -\frac{1}{p}+4p & \frac{1}{p}-3p & 0 \\ \frac{1}{p}-3p & -\frac{1}{3p}+2+3p & -\frac{1}{3p} \\ 0 & -\frac{1}{3p} & \frac{2}{3p} \end{bmatrix},$$

$$\begin{bmatrix} I \\ 0 \\ 0 \end{bmatrix} = \mathbf{Y}\begin{bmatrix} V_1 \\ V_2 \\ V_3 \end{bmatrix}, \quad \text{or}$$

$$I = \left(-\frac{1}{p}+4p\right)V_1+\left(\frac{1}{p}-3p\right)V_2,$$

$$0 = \left(\frac{1}{p}-3p\right)V_1+\left(-\frac{1}{3p}+2+3p\right)V_2-\frac{1}{3p}V_3,$$

$$0 = -\frac{1}{3p}V_2+\frac{2}{3p}V_3.$$

CHAPTER 6

Three-phase Networks

THREE-PHASE networks of any complexity can be analysed by the use of the connection matrix as explained in Chapter 5. To illustrate this consider the simple case of a three-phase network shown in Fig. 14.

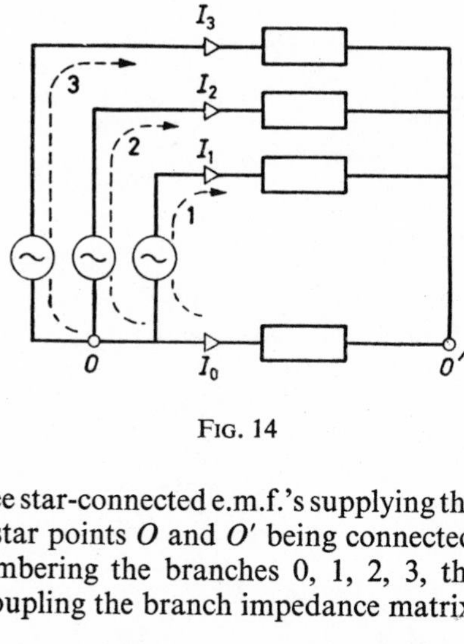

FIG. 14

This shows three star-connected e.m.f.'s supplying three star-connected impedances, the star points O and O' being connected through another impedance. Numbering the branches 0, 1, 2, 3, then in the general case of mutual coupling the branch impedance matrix is

$$[z_{ik}] = \begin{bmatrix} z_{00} & z_{01} & z_{02} & z_{03} \\ z_{01} & z_{11} & z_{12} & z_{13} \\ z_{02} & z_{12} & z_{22} & z_{23} \\ z_{03} & z_{13} & z_{23} & z_{33} \end{bmatrix}.$$

z_{11}, z_{22}, z_{33} are the impedances of the three star-connected branches and z_{00} the impedance of the neutral conductor. z_{12}, z_{13}, z_{23} are the mutual impedances between the star-connected branches and z_{01}, z_{02}, z_{03} are those between these branches and the impedance in the neutral. By choosing the meshes as indicated in the figure the mesh currents can be made equal to the line currents and the connection matrix assumes the form

$$\mathbf{C} = \begin{bmatrix} -1 & 1 & 0 & 0 \\ -1 & 0 & 1 & 0 \\ -1 & 0 & 0 & 1 \end{bmatrix}.$$

The mesh impedance matrix is then the 3×3 matrix

$$\mathbf{Z} = \begin{bmatrix} Z_{11} & Z_{12} & Z_{13} \\ Z_{12} & Z_{22} & Z_{23} \\ Z_{13} & Z_{23} & Z_{33} \end{bmatrix}$$

$$= \begin{bmatrix} -1 & 1 & 0 & 0 \\ -1 & 0 & 1 & 0 \\ -1 & 0 & 0 & 1 \end{bmatrix} \begin{bmatrix} z_{00} & z_{01} & z_{02} & z_{03} \\ z_{01} & z_{11} & z_{12} & z_{13} \\ z_{02} & z_{12} & z_{22} & z_{23} \\ z_{03} & z_{13} & z_{23} & z_{33} \end{bmatrix} \begin{bmatrix} -1 & -1 & -1 \\ 1 & 0 & 0 \\ 0 & 1 & 0 \\ 0 & 0 & 1 \end{bmatrix}, \qquad (40)$$

so that

$$\begin{aligned} Z_{11} &= z_{00}-2z_{01}+z_{11}, & Z_{12} &= z_{00}-z_{01}-z_{02}+z_{12}, \\ Z_{22} &= z_{00}-2z_{02}+z_{22}, & Z_{13} &= z_{00}-z_{01}-z_{03}+z_{13}, \\ Z_{33} &= z_{00}-2z_{03}+z_{33}, & Z_{23} &= z_{00}-z_{02}-z_{03}+z_{23}. \end{aligned} \qquad (41)$$

The line currents I_1, I_2, I_3 can then be determined from the equation

$$\mathbf{E} = \mathbf{ZI},$$

where **E** is the column vector formed by the star-connected phase e.m.f.'s E_1, E_2, E_3. I_0 can then be determined from the equation

$$I_0+I_1+I_2+I_3 = 0.$$

Now, as already stated, equations (40) and (41) hold in the most general case when mutual coupling is present. For certain special cases the matrix **Z** assumes a simpler form and some of these will now be considered.

6·1 Balanced networks

In this case the impedances of the three branches are the same, so that $z_{11}=z_{22}=z_{33}$ and moreover $z_{12}=z_{23}=z_{13}$ and $z_{01}=z_{02}=z_{03}$. Substituting these values into equations (41) we see that

$$Z_{11} = Z_{22} = Z_{33} = Z_p \quad \text{say,}$$

and

$$Z_{12} = Z_{23} = Z_{13} = Z_m \quad \text{say.}$$

The mesh impedance matrix therefore has the form

$$\mathbf{Z} = \begin{bmatrix} Z_p & Z_m & Z_m \\ Z_m & Z_p & Z_m \\ Z_m & Z_m & Z_p \end{bmatrix}.$$

Hence a balanced network of mutual impedances and an impedance in neutral can be replaced by an equivalent network with a self-impedance Z_p in each phase and a mutual impedance Z_m between phases, but with no neutral impedance.

6·2 Balanced networks and balanced e.m.f.'s

The magnitudes and phase relationships of the e.m.f.'s E_1, E_2 and E_3 can be quite general. Assuming, however, a balanced set of e.m.f.'s of positive phase sequence, i.e. assuming that their magnitudes are the same, that their phase sequence is 1, 2, 3 and that the phase difference between them is 120 degrees, or $2\pi/3$ radians, we can write

$$E_1 = E, \qquad E_2 = \alpha^2 E, \qquad E_3 = \alpha E.$$

α denotes the familiar complex operator $\epsilon^{j2\pi/3}$ which rotates a vector through an angle $2\pi/3$ radians in the positive (counter-clockwise) sense.

Clearly $$\alpha^3 = \epsilon^{j2\pi} = 1, \qquad 1+\alpha+\alpha^2 = 0.$$

We then have, using the result of §6·1,

$$\begin{bmatrix} E \\ \alpha^2 E \\ \alpha E \end{bmatrix} = \begin{bmatrix} Z_p & Z_m & Z_m \\ Z_m & Z_p & Z_m \\ Z_m & Z_m & Z_p \end{bmatrix} \begin{bmatrix} I_1 \\ I_2 \\ I_3 \end{bmatrix},$$

where $$I_1 = I, \qquad I_2 = \alpha^2 I, \qquad I_3 = \alpha I.$$

Thus $$E = (Z_p + \alpha^2 Z_m + \alpha Z_m) I = (Z_p - Z_m) I,$$

since $\alpha + \alpha^2 = -1$.

This forms a justification for the normal single-phase representation of balanced three-phase networks.

6·3 Impedance matrix for rotating machines

It can be shown that in the case of rotating machines the impedance matrix assumes the form

$$\mathbf{Z} = \begin{bmatrix} A & C & B \\ B & A & C \\ C & B & A \end{bmatrix}.$$

From physical considerations it is easily seen that, unlike the case of §6·2, B and C must be distinct, for in a rotating machine the *second* phase is related to the *first* phase, not in the same way as the *third* phase to the *first* phase, but as the *third* phase to the *second* phase or the *first* to the *third* phase. This matrix will be used again later in connection with symmetrical components.

6·4 Symmetrical components

Let us suppose that three given voltages E_a, E_b, E_c are not balanced. We wish to determine, if possible, three voltages E_0, E_1 and E_2 such that the voltages E_a, E_b, E_c can be expressed in terms of E_0, E_1, E_2 in the following manner.

$$\begin{aligned} E_a &= E_0 + E_1 + E_2, \\ E_b &= E_0 + \alpha^2 E_1 + \alpha E_2, \\ E_c &= E_0 + \alpha E_1 + \alpha^2 E_2. \end{aligned} \tag{42}$$

Equation (42) may be written in matrix form

$$\begin{bmatrix} E_a \\ E_b \\ E_c \end{bmatrix} = \begin{bmatrix} 1 & 1 & 1 \\ 1 & \alpha^2 & \alpha \\ 1 & \alpha & \alpha^2 \end{bmatrix} \begin{bmatrix} E_0 \\ E_1 \\ E_2 \end{bmatrix}. \tag{43}$$

Writing $\mathbf{T} = \begin{bmatrix} 1 & 1 & 1 \\ 1 & \alpha^2 & \alpha \\ 1 & \alpha & \alpha^2 \end{bmatrix}$,

we have

$$|\mathbf{T}| = \begin{vmatrix} 1 & 1 & 3 \\ 1 & \alpha^2 & 1+\alpha+\alpha^2 \\ 1 & \alpha & 1+\alpha+\alpha^2 \end{vmatrix} \quad \text{(adding columns 1 and 2 to column 3)}$$

$$= 3(\alpha-\alpha^2), \quad \text{since} \quad 1+\alpha+\alpha^2 = 0.$$

Thus $|\mathbf{T}| \neq 0$, and

$$\mathbf{T}^{-1} = \frac{1}{3(\alpha-\alpha^2)} \begin{bmatrix} \alpha-\alpha^2 & \alpha-\alpha^2 & \alpha-\alpha^2 \\ \alpha-\alpha^2 & \alpha^2-1 & 1-\alpha \\ \alpha-\alpha^2 & 1-\alpha & \alpha^2-1 \end{bmatrix}$$

$$= \frac{1}{3}\begin{bmatrix} 1 & 1 & 1 \\ 1 & -\dfrac{\alpha+1}{\alpha} & \dfrac{1}{\alpha} \\ 1 & \dfrac{1}{\alpha} & -\dfrac{\alpha+1}{\alpha} \end{bmatrix}$$

$$= \frac{1}{3}\begin{bmatrix} 1 & 1 & 1 \\ 1 & \alpha & \alpha^2 \\ 1 & \alpha^2 & \alpha \end{bmatrix}.$$

Equations (43) therefore have a unique solution given by

$$\begin{bmatrix} E_0 \\ E_1 \\ E_2 \end{bmatrix} = \mathbf{T}^{-1}\begin{bmatrix} E_a \\ E_b \\ E_c \end{bmatrix} = \frac{1}{3}\begin{bmatrix} 1 & 1 & 1 \\ 1 & \alpha & \alpha^2 \\ 1 & \alpha^2 & \alpha \end{bmatrix}\begin{bmatrix} E_a \\ E_b \\ E_c \end{bmatrix}.$$

E_0, E_1, E_2 are known as the *symmetrical components* of the unbalanced voltages E_a, E_b, E_c.

Precisely the same equations hold if we replace voltages by currents. Now

$$\begin{bmatrix} E_a \\ E_b \\ E_c \end{bmatrix} = \mathbf{Z}\begin{bmatrix} I_a \\ I_b \\ I_c \end{bmatrix}, \tag{44}$$

where $\mathbf{Z}$ is the impedance matrix for the network, calculated as in Chapter 5. It follows that

$$\mathbf{T}\begin{bmatrix} E_0 \\ E_1 \\ E_2 \end{bmatrix} = \mathbf{ZT}\begin{bmatrix} I_0 \\ I_1 \\ I_2 \end{bmatrix},$$

and pre-multiplying by $\mathbf{T}^{-1}$ we obtain

$$\begin{bmatrix} E_0 \\ E_1 \\ E_2 \end{bmatrix} = \mathbf{T}^{-1}\mathbf{ZT}\begin{bmatrix} I_0 \\ I_1 \\ I_2 \end{bmatrix}. \tag{45}$$

Thus the new impedance matrix is of the form $\mathbf{T}^{-1}\mathbf{ZT}$.

In general equations (45) are no simpler than equations (44), for in both cases we have the same number of equations and the same number of unknowns. However in some cases, when the matrix $\mathbf{Z}$ has certain kinds of symmetry, the matrix $\mathbf{T}^{-1}\mathbf{ZT}$ assumes a very simple form (in particular diagonal form) and the introduction of symmetrical components then has great advantages.

We shall take as examples the two matrices **Z** of §6·1 and §6·3. First let

$$\mathbf{Z} = \begin{bmatrix} Z_p & Z_m & Z_m \\ Z_m & Z_p & Z_m \\ Z_m & Z_m & Z_p \end{bmatrix}.$$

The eigenvalues of **Z** are given by

$$\begin{vmatrix} Z_p-\lambda & Z_m & Z_m \\ Z_m & Z_p-\lambda & Z_m \\ Z_m & Z_m & Z_p-\lambda \end{vmatrix} = 0.$$

Adding columns 2 and 3 to column 1, and subtracting column 3 from column 2,

$$\begin{vmatrix} Z_p+2Z_m-\lambda & 0 & Z_m \\ Z_p+2Z_m-\lambda & Z_p-Z_m-\lambda & Z_m \\ Z_p+2Z_m-\lambda & Z_m-Z_p+\lambda & Z_p-\lambda \end{vmatrix} = 0,$$

i.e. $$(Z_p+2Z_m-\lambda)(Z_p-Z_m-\lambda)\begin{vmatrix} 1 & 0 & Z_m \\ 1 & 1 & Z_m \\ 1 & -1 & Z_p-\lambda \end{vmatrix} = 0,$$

i.e. $$(Z_p+2Z_m-\lambda)(Z_p-Z_m-\lambda)^2 = 0.$$

The eigenvalues are Z_p+2Z_m, Z_p-Z_m, Z_p-Z_m and the reader will easily verify that the corresponding eigenvectors may be taken to be $\{1\ 1\ 1\}$, $\{1\ \alpha^2\ \alpha\}$, $\{1\ \alpha\ \alpha^2\}$. These are the columns of the matrix **T**, so that

$$\mathbf{T}^{-1}\mathbf{Z}\mathbf{T} = \begin{bmatrix} Z_p+2Z_m & 0 & 0 \\ 0 & Z_p-Z_m & 0 \\ 0 & 0 & Z_p-Z_m \end{bmatrix}.$$

Thus $$\mathbf{T}^{-1}\begin{bmatrix} E_a \\ E_b \\ E_c \end{bmatrix} = \begin{bmatrix} E_0 \\ E_1 \\ E_2 \end{bmatrix} = \begin{bmatrix} (Z_p+2Z_m)I_0 \\ (Z_p-Z_m)I_1 \\ (Z_p-Z_m)I_2 \end{bmatrix},$$

or $$\begin{bmatrix} I_0 \\ I_1 \\ I_2 \end{bmatrix} = \begin{bmatrix} E_0/(Z_p+2Z_m) \\ E_1/(Z_p-Z_m) \\ E_2/(Z_p-Z_m) \end{bmatrix}$$

and
$$\begin{bmatrix} I_a \\ I_b \\ I_c \end{bmatrix} = \mathbf{T} \begin{bmatrix} I_0 \\ I_1 \\ I_2 \end{bmatrix}.$$

Finally take
$$\mathbf{Z} = \begin{bmatrix} A & C & B \\ B & A & C \\ C & B & A \end{bmatrix}.$$

The reader will verify by inspection that $\lambda = A+B+C$, $A+B\alpha+C\alpha^2$, $A+B\alpha^2+C\alpha$ are roots of the equation
$$\begin{vmatrix} A-\lambda & C & B \\ B & A-\lambda & C \\ C & B & A-\lambda \end{vmatrix} = 0.$$

For when $\lambda = A+B+C$, the sum of the three columns of the determinant is zero. When $\lambda = A+B\alpha+C\alpha^2$, column $1+\alpha^2 \times$ column $2+\alpha \times$ column $3=0$, and similarly when $\lambda = A+B\alpha^2+C\alpha$. These three values are therefore the eigenvalues of the matrix **Z** and the corresponding eigenvectors are easily seen to be $\{1\ 1\ 1\}$, $\{1\ \alpha^2\ \alpha\}$, $\{1\ \alpha\ \alpha^2\}$. Hence, in the same way as before,
$$\mathbf{T}^{-1}\mathbf{Z}\mathbf{T} = \begin{bmatrix} A+B+C & 0 & 0 \\ 0 & A+B\alpha+C\alpha^2 & 0 \\ 0 & 0 & A+B\alpha^2+C\alpha \end{bmatrix}$$

and
$$\begin{bmatrix} E_0 \\ E_1 \\ E_2 \end{bmatrix} = \begin{bmatrix} (A+B+C)I_0 \\ (A+B\alpha+C\alpha^2)I_1 \\ (A+B\alpha^2+C\alpha)I_2 \end{bmatrix}.$$

I_a, I_b, I_c can be determined immediately as in the previous example.

Answers to Examples

Examples 1

3. $x = 1, \quad y = -1, \quad z = 2.$

4. $\mathbf{X} = \frac{1}{2}\begin{bmatrix} 15 & 13 \\ 16 & 14 \end{bmatrix}, \quad \mathbf{Y} = \frac{1}{4}\begin{bmatrix} 33 & 19 \\ 43 & 25 \end{bmatrix}.$

5. $\begin{bmatrix} -2 & 0 \\ 0 & -2 \end{bmatrix}, \quad \begin{bmatrix} -1 & 0 \\ 0 & -1 \end{bmatrix}, \quad \begin{bmatrix} -2 & 0 \\ c & -1 \end{bmatrix},$

$\begin{bmatrix} -2 & b \\ 0 & -1 \end{bmatrix}, \quad \begin{bmatrix} -1 & 0 \\ c & -2 \end{bmatrix}, \quad \begin{bmatrix} -1 & b \\ 0 & -2 \end{bmatrix}.$

b and c are arbitrary.

Examples 2

1. $\mathbf{Y} = \mathbf{X}^{(1)} + 2\mathbf{X}^{(2)} + 3\mathbf{X}^{(3)}.$

3. $\begin{bmatrix} 4 & -1 & 0 & 0 \\ 5 & -1 & 0 & 0 \\ -98 & 22 & 3 & 1 \\ -75 & 17 & 2 & 1 \end{bmatrix}.$

4. $\mathbf{A} = \begin{bmatrix} 13 & -5 \\ -5 & 13 \end{bmatrix}, \quad X^2/4 + Y^2/9 = 1.$

Examples 3

1. $\mathbf{Q} = \begin{bmatrix} 1 & 0 & 1 \\ 0 & 1 & 0 \\ 1 & 0 & -1 \end{bmatrix}, \quad \mathbf{Q}^{-1}\mathbf{A}\mathbf{Q} = \begin{bmatrix} 1 & 0 & 0 \\ 0 & 1 & 0 \\ 0 & 0 & -1 \end{bmatrix}.$

2. $\mathbf{A}^n = \frac{1}{3}\begin{bmatrix} 4.2^n + (-1)^{n+1} & 4.2^n + 4(-1)^{n+1} \\ -2^n + (-1)^n & -2^n + 4(-1)^n \end{bmatrix}.$

$$3.\ \mathbf{Q} = \begin{bmatrix} 1/\sqrt{2} & 0 & 1/\sqrt{2} \\ 0 & 1 & 0 \\ -1/\sqrt{2} & 0 & 1/\sqrt{2} \end{bmatrix}, \qquad \mathbf{Q}^t\mathbf{AQ} = \begin{bmatrix} 4 & 0 & 0 \\ 0 & 9 & 0 \\ 0 & 0 & 36 \end{bmatrix}.$$

4. $x = z = 0; \quad x+z = y = 0; \quad x-z = y = 0.$

Bibliography

1. FRAZER, R. A., DUNCAN, W. J., and COLLAR, A. R., *Elementary Matrices and some Applications to Dynamics and Differential Equations* (Cambridge University Press, 1960).
2. AITKEN, A. C., *Determinants and Matrices* (Oliver and Boyd, 1942).
3. BIRKHOFF, G. and MACLANE, S., *A Survey of Modern Algebra* (Macmillan, New York, 1950), Chapters VI to X inclusive. This is written from the point of view of the pure mathematician rather than the engineer, but it is elementary.
4. SHEA, R. F., *Principles of Transistor Circuits* (John Wiley, 1953).
5. KOENIG, H. E. and BLACKWELL, W. A., *Electromechanical System Theory* (McGraw-Hill, 1961).
6. MORTLOCK, J. R. and HUMPHREY DAVIES, M. W., *Power System Analysis* (Chapman and Hall, 1952).
7. STIGANT, S. A., *Modern Electrical Engineering Mathematics* (Hutchinson, 1946).

Index